THE
SCOTTISH
QUIZ BOOK

By

LAWRENCE STENHOUSE

Illustrated by STANLEY SMITH

ERNEST BENN LIMITED

LONDON · 1957

First Published 1957 by Ernest Benn Limited
Bouverie House · Fleet Street · London · EC4

Printed in Great Britain

Author's Preface

WE HOPE that you will find this book both entertaining and informative, and that it will help you to know Scotland better. Much of Scotland's lore has been handed down by word of mouth and various versions exist, so that you may find that our version differs slightly from the one with which you are familiar; yet it will be recognisable and these slight differences should not trouble you. I should like to thank my friends, colleagues and pupils for helping to make the book varied and interesting and to acknowledge the helpfulness of the staffs of Dunfermline Public Library and the Mitchell Library, Glasgow. If any error has escaped our careful checking we should be glad to hear of it.

LAWRENCE STENHOUSE
Dunfermline, 1957

Contents

Scotch Broth

1 What is 'The Royal Mile'?

2 How long is a Scots mile?

3 What is a 'Munro'?

4 Who were Burke and Hare?

5 What is the meaning of Holyrood?

6 Of what county is Dumbarton the county town?

7 What is the Great Cumbrae?

8 How many players are there in a shinty team?

9 What great Scottish disaster occurred in 1879?

10 'I'll meet you at the Shell.' Where is that?

11 Can you list the Scottish universities in order of their age?

12 Here are a number of place-names associated with particular foods. The list of foods opposite them has been jumbled. Can you set the correct food after each place-name:

A Forfar   cheese
B Loch Fyne   cake
C Edinburgh   bannock
D Dundee   smokies (smoked haddock)
E Selkirk   kippers (or herring)
F Arbroath   rock
G Dunlop   bridies

13 Where would you find a cairn erected to the memory of John Cobb?

14 What are the ingredients of a haggis?

15 Where is 'doon the watter'?

16 From what historical event did the town of Portobello derive its name?

17 What is a clachan?

18 Which Scottish university has an annual historical procession called the 'Kate Kennedy Procession'?

Scotch Broth

19 What is a 'salmon ladder'?

20 Which saint's symbol is used on the flag of Scotland?

21 Which is the patron saint of Glasgow?

22
2 doits	1 bodle
2 bodles	1 plack
40 placks	1 merk

What is being reckoned in this table?

23 In what Scottish village is Pontius Pilate reputed to have been born?

24 What is the oldest building in Edinburgh?

25 Where would you find:
A Devil's Point and Angel's Peak?
B Hell and the Elysian Fields?

26 Why is Scotland Yard so called?

27 What is Mons Meg?

28 How does John O' Groats get its name?

29 Where is the Kitchener Memorial Tower?

30 Who owns the foreshore in Scotland?

31 Which is the oldest tree in Scotland?

32 What and where are the Elgin marbles?

33 How many lakes are there in Scotland?

34 Who was 'The Scottish Hogarth'?

35 Who wrote a piece of music known as *Fingal's Cave*?

36 When was the Forth Bridge opened?

37 What is the national emblem of Scotland?

38 Who is Auld Hornie?

39 How large is a Scots pint?

40 Where does President Eisenhower of the United States have a residence in Scotland?

41 When was an Empire Exhibition last held in Glasgow?

42 Grouse, Partridge, Pheasant
Can you arrange these game birds in order of their size?

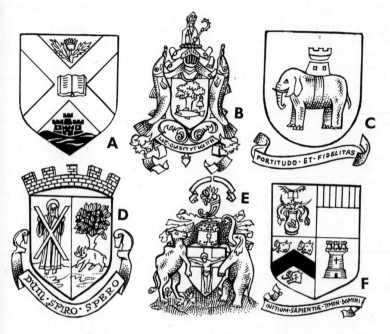

43 Can you name the coats of arms in the illustration above?

44 The purchase of 'Le Christ' by Salvador Dali recently aroused widespread comment in Scotland. By what art gallery was it purchased?

45 What are the Lanark Stone, the Linlithgow Firlot, the Stirling Stoup and the Edinburgh Ell?

46 Who was Madeleine Smith?

47 Who is Para Handy?

48 Where in Scotland would you find a reindeer herd?

49 What island off the Atlantic coast of Scotland was annexed by Great Britain in 1955?

50 On what Scottish mountain did Maskelyne conduct his famous experiments to measure the earth's density?

Scottish Life

1 In which towns are these famous schools:
- A Daniel Stewart's College
- B Morgan Academy
- C Madras College
- D Alan Glen's School
- E Marr College
- F Webster's Seminary
- G Bell Baxter School
- H Robert Gordon's College
- I Morrison's Academy
- J The Nicolson Institute

2 In which towns are the following Scottish daily papers published:
- A *The Press and Journal*
- B *The Scotsman*
- C *The Herald*
- D *The Courier and Advertiser*
- E *The Record*

3 Which castles are seats of the following people:
- A Duke of Argyll
- B Chief of the Clan McLeod
- C Earl of Strathmore
- D Duke of Roxburghe
- E Duke of Sutherland

4 What famous castles are illustrated on the opposite page?

5 To what studies are the following colleges devoted:
- A Jordanhill College
- B The Heriot-Watt College
- C Dunfermline College, Aberdeen

6 Can you give the dates of the following red letter days in the Scottish Calendar:
- A Hogmanay
- B Hallowe'en
- C St. Andrew's Day
- D Lammas

7 In which cities are these famous streets:
- A Union Street
- B Sauchiehall Street
- C Princes Street

8 Where is the principal Glasgow Art Collection housed?

9 Where is the Scottish Motor Show held?

10 On what figures are rates on houses levied in Scotland?

11 Where is the General Assembly held?

12 What is the General Assembly?

13 Where is a gun fired at 1 p.m. every day?

A

B

C

D

Scottish Life

14 Who is the principal Law Officer in Scotland?

15 What is the title of the chief criminal judge in Scotland?

16 What is the title of the chief civil judge?

17 What criminal verdict is found in Scotland but not in England and Wales?

18 What is the title of the judge who normally presides in the Sheriff Court?

19 Which is the oldest Scottish Academy?

20 Which is the largest university?

21 What is 'Meal Monday'?

22 Which is the oldest Scottish newspaper with a continuous existence from its foundation to the present day?

23 Which member of the crew of a ship is traditionally Scots in fiction?

24 What is 'The Hielan'man's Umbrella'?

25 What is a bailie?

26 What is bee baw babbity?

27 When would you expect 'a first foot'?

28 When is Hansel Monday?

29 If you were a dux, what would you be?

30 What is a 'gillie'?

31 When would you expect to find people carrying turnip lanterns?

32 If a Scotsman used 'Murray's Diary', what would he use it for?

33 Who is 'Tammy Troot'?

34 For what purpose is a university rectorial held?

35 What is the name of the headquarters of the Civil Service in Scotland?

36 What are 'The Citizens' and 'The Gateway'?

37 What is feu duty?

38 Who are the 'Broons'?

A Guid Scots Tongue

1 What are the following articles of Highland dress:
A A fillibeg
B A skean-dhu
C A sporran
D A brogue

2 Can you identify the following living things:
A A stirk
B A hairy worm
C A spinning Maggie
D A foumart
E A herling
F A Virgin Mary
G A forkie tailie
H A puddock
I A speug
J Imaky-amaky

3 What would you be doing if you were to:
A Keep a calm sough
B Ca' canny
C Tak' tent
D Mak siccar

4 What are the following:
A A black saxpence
B A stickit minister
C A wag at the wa'
D A tarry breeks
E MacFarlane's lantern
F A Lochaber trump
G A white Geordie
H A tattie bogle
I A cutty sark
J A bubbly jock
K A kist o' whistles
L A lum hat
M A blue mogganer
N A chuckie stane
O A tattie howker
P A bonnet laird
Q A Glasgow magistrate
R A guid dochter
S A muckle joarum
T An Andrea Ferrara
U A kenspeckle figure
V A cuttin' loaf
W Nicky Tams
X A Flatterin' Friday
Y Cauld kail het again
Z Ba' siller

5 Can you give the meaning of these expressive adjectives:
A Eldritch
B Fleering
C Peched
D Reaming
E Dreich
F Couthy
G Gurlie
H Sleekit
I Wairsh
J Wabbit

6 Where is 'ben the hoose'?

A Guid Scots Tongue

7 What do we mean when we say that a person is:
   A Pernickety
   B Ill-faured
   C Muckle-moued
   D Thrawn
   E Glaikit
   F Contramashious
   G Sonsie
   H Lang-nebbit
   I Drouthy
   J Pawky
   K Caur-handit
   L Biddable
   M Douce
   N Brosy heidit
   O Hummel-drummel
   P Jimp
   Q Fushionless
   R Fey
   S Dour
   T Unco guid

8 What are the following dishes:
   A Powsowdie
   B Cock-a-leekie
   C Muslin kail
   D Partan bree
   E Chappit tatties
   F Drammach

9 What are the following:
   A Airts
   B Blethers
   C Corn rigs
   D Whigmaleeries
   E Clash-ma-clavers
   F Flichtmafleathers
   G Wally dogs
   H Quinies and loonies
   I Glameries
   J Chapman billies
   K Usqueba
   L Orramen
   M Caterans
   N East coast haars
   O Dominies
   P Chittering bites
   Q Pieces
   R Elf arrows
   S Tweedledees
   T Lobby dossers

10 What are the modern names of these towns:
    A Aberbrothok
    B Cadzow
    C Jethart
    D Kilrymont

11 What is a by-name?

12 What is the meaning of 'The Trossachs'?

13 What is your pinkie?

14 If you were told just to lift the 'sneck', what would you do?

15 What does tapsalteerie mean?

16 What is the meaning of 'Ceud mile failte'?

17 Are you a haaflin?

Scotland in Arms

1 Which Scottish regiment is the senior infantry regiment of the British Army?

2 Can you give the popular names of the following regiments:
   A The Royal Highland Regiment
   B The Scottish Rifles
   C The Second Dragoons

3 Can you identify these regiments:
   A Pontius Pilate's Bodyguard
   B The Earl o' Mar's Greybreeks
   C The Ross-shire Buffs
   D The Glesca Keelies
   E The Rory's

4 Which is the oldest highland regiment?

5 Why is the wreck of the *Birkenhead* in 1852 famous in Scottish military history?

6 Which regiment marches past to *The Daughter of the Regiment* when on parade before royalty, and why?

7 Which tartans do these military units (past or present) have in common:

   A The Royal Scots; The Canadian Scottish Regiment; The Pretoria Highlanders; The Scottish Platoon of the 2nd Selangor Battalion, Federated Malay States Volunteer Force

   B The Argyll and Sutherland Highlanders; The New South Wales Scottish Regiment; The Royal Highland Regiment of Canada; The New Zealand Scottish

   C The Gordon Highlanders; The Victorian Scottish Regiment The Cape Town Highlanders; The Scottish Company of the Hong Kong Volunteer Defence Corps

8 Why do you think that there are Scottish regiments throughout the Commonwealth?

Scotland in Arms

9   Which Scottish regiments have the following mottoes:

    A Second to None   c Sans Peur

    B Bydand (Waiting)   D Strike Sure

10   Of which regiments are the following the depots:

    A Churchill Barracks, Ayr

    B Winston Barracks, Lanark

    c Maryhill Barracks, Glasgow

    D Queen's Barracks, Perth

    E Fort George, Inverness-shire

    F The Castle, Stirling

11   What is the kilt of the London Scottish and Toronto Scottish Regiments? Can you describe its appearance?

12   Where do the Seaforth Highlanders get their name?

13   What was 'The Green Brigade' which included MacKay's Highlanders, Stargate's Corps and Lumsden's Musketeers?

14   Which regiment uses 'Lochaber No More' as its 'Lights Out'?

15   Who designed the Scottish War Memorial?

16   Who was Sir Alexander Leslie?

17   What were the *fencibles*?

18   Which weapon of war is shared by Scottish and some Irish regiments?

19   Who is Gold Stick-in-waiting for Scotland?

20   Which regiment is Princess Louise's?

21   On what part of Scottish uniforms might a blackcock's tail be found?

22   Which Scottish regiment was the famous 'Thin Red Line' at Balaclava and is consequently the only infantry regiment to bear the battle honour, 'Balaclava' on its colours?

23   Which Scottish regiment is known by its red hackle?

24   The Guards Regiments are distinguished by the arrangement of their buttons in ones, twos, threes, fours and fives. Which is the arrangement of the Scots Guards?

25   Which regiments comprise 'The Lowland Brigade'?

26   Which regiments comprise 'The Highland Brigade'?

27   To what regiments, in what year, did the soldiers in the drawing opposite belong?

Scotland in Arms

28 Which regiment carries its rifles to church?

29 Only one man in the British army could be seen wearing a white bearskin cap with a red plume. Who?

30 Which Scottish regiment is entitled to wear Minden Roses on the anniversary of the Battle of Minden (1st August, 1759)?

31 Which army unit is commemorated by a famous memorial at Spean Bridge?

32 Which famous Scottish soldier was murdered in Khartoum?

33 What is the name of the great naval base in Orkney?

34 What important forces establishment is situated in Rosyth?

35 What is a Lochaber axe?

36 Which Scot was Naval Commander-in-Chief in the Mediterranean during the last war at the time of the Battles of Taranto and Matapan?

37 Which famous Scottish soldier effected the relief of Lucknow in the Indian Mutiny?

38 Which famous Scottish soldier died in Spain in the moment of victory after leading his troops in a heroic march?

39 Of which Scottish regiments are these the marches:
A *The Keel Row*
B *Dumbarton's Drums*
C *Within a Mile of Edinburgh Toun*
D *Cock o' the North*
E *The Campbells are Coming*
F *The Wee Cooper o' Fife*

40 Which regiment plays no music when going to or returning from church on Sundays?

41 What honour fell to a bugler of the Scots Guards on 8th May, 1945?

———————★———————

Traditions of the Borders and Lowlands

1 Can you identify the following:

   A A border hero treacherously hanged with all his men at Caerlanrigg by James V

   B A border character who stole a horse and was paid by its owner for a foal he had never lost

   C A border hero who was taken in a truce but rescued from Carlisle Castle by the bold Buccleuch

   D A character who set off to recover three stolen cows and came home with three fine horses

   E An English outlaw who helped to set Jock o' the Side free, but was later betrayed by the Armstrongs

2 What is the Devil's Dyke?

3 Where would you find the keys of the old Tolbooth of Edinburgh and what was the old Tolbooth?

4 Where would you find:

   A Little France (Little Picardy)

   B Little Egypt

5 Who were the Faa?

6 Where is Tibbie Shiel's Inn and why is it famous?

7 Where do the 'uppies' play the 'doonies' at Candlemas?

8 Who was Black Agnes?

9 Who cleft the Eildon Hills in three?

10 Melrose, Jedburgh, Kelso
   What do these three have in common?

11 When Auld Wat of Harden was served with spurs on a dish what did that mean?

12 Who was 'Bell the Cat'?

13 Who was 'Muckle-Mou'ed Meg'?

14 What family is associated with Branksome tower?

15 What is a moss trooper?

Traditions of the Borders and Lowlands

16 Whose ghost might you meet on Magus Muir?

17 What is the alternative name of the Battle of Otterburn?

18 Who said:

> 'Yestreen the Queen had four Maries,
> The nicht she'll hae but three;
> There was Marie Seton, and Mary Beaton,
> And Marie Carmichael and me.'

19 Who was the Laird o' Cockpen?

20 What was the Bateable Land?

21 Where do the Braw Lads gather at Midsummer?

22 Where do the callants ride the Marches under a cornet?

23 Which border town was renowned for its soutars?

24 How did Queensferry get its name?

25 Who were the Wigtownshire martyrs?

26 In which village is a dowry given to the tallest, shortest, oldest and youngest brides of the year?

27 Edinburgh's big but . . . ?

28 Who was Tom Purdie?

29 What Border abbey was founded by Devorguilla, the foundress of Balliol College, Oxford?

30 What was the Luckenbooth?

31 For what is Jenny Geddes remembered?

32 What is Arthur's Seat?

33 What is the Ruthwell Cross?

34 In which castle in Scotland could you find a bottle dungeon?

35 From which castle did Mary Queen of Scots escape by boat?

36 Which spendthrift lost all his possessions and recovered them with money he found at a rope's end?

37 Which great King of Scots was originally Earl of Carrick and Lord of Annandale?

38 Who was Thomas of Ercildoune?

39 Where did he lie?

40 Where are 'The Dowie Dens'?

Transport and Communications

1 What stretches of water do these ferries cross?
  A Ballachulish Ferry
  B Queensferry Passage
  C Strome Ferry
  D Kessock Ferry
  E Erskine Ferry

2 Between which towns do these trains run?
  A The Heart of Midlothian
  B The North Briton
  C The Queen of Scots
  D The Fife Coast Express
  E The Aberdonian

3 In which towns are these railway stations?
  A Haymarket
  B Gilmour Street
  C Buchanan Street
  D Tay Bridge
  E St. Enoch

4 Which aerodrome serves these places?
  A Edinburgh   D Glasgow
  B Shetland   E Aberdeen
  C Inverness

5 Can you identify these early Scottish railways from their
   initials?
  A C.R.   D N.B.R.
  B G.N.S.R.   E H.R.
  C G.S.W.R.

6 Where are these lighthouses?
  A The Cloch   D Girdle Ness
  B St. Abb's   E The Bell Rock
  C The Bass Rock

Transport and Communications

7 Can you identify the bridges in the picture opposite?

8 Can you identify the following routes?

   A By Tummel and Loch Rannoch and Lochaber.

   B   'cross the ford,
     Where in the snaw the chapman smoor'd;
     And past the birks and meikle stane,
     Where drunken Charlie Brak's neck-bane;
     And thro' the whins and by the cairn,
     Where hunters fand the murder'd bairn; . . .'

   C Glenfinnan, Blair Atholl, Perth, Stirling, Falkirk, Edinburgh, Prestonpans, Hawick, Carlisle, Preston, Manchester, Derby.

9 Can you identify:

   A The longest bridge in Scotland
   B The tallest bridge in Scotland
   C The largest swing bridge in Scotland

10 Can you name the chief port in each of these areas?

   A The Firth of Forth
   B The west coast of Scotland
   C The north coast of Scotland

11 Which famous railway bridge spans the Tweed at Berwick?

12 What is the Lairig Ghru?

13 Which was the first railway in Scotland?

14 Which was the first Scottish railway to use steam locomotives?

15 How many canals are there in Scotland and what are their names?

16 What is a 'puffer'?

17 Which is the longest railway tunnel in Scotland?

18 Which Scottish river has a passenger tunnel beneath it?

19 What are snow posts?

20 What is 'Neptune's Staircase'?

21 Which is the most northerly town in Britain to be reached by railway?

Transport and Communications

A

B

C

D

Transport and Communications

22 What have these in common?
The Marchioness of Breadalbane, The Duchess of Rothesay, The Duchess of Fife, The Duchess of Montrose, The Marchioness of Lorne.

23 Where is the highest main line railway in Britain?

24 What are drove roads and what are Wade's roads?

25 What is the meaning of the place name, Tarbert or Tarbet?

26 What is the 'Rest and Be Thankful'?

27 Can you name the only Scottish made motor road vehicle?

28 What lochs form part of the Caledonian Canal?

29 Which is the highest main road in Scotland?

30 Which was the first Clyde steamer?

31 Argyll and Seil Island: Bernera and Lewis. What have these two pairs in common?

32 Can you name a Scottish aircraft developed for use on small landing fields such as are found in the Scottish islands?

33 What do Kirk o' Shotts and Meldrum have in common?

34 In which Scottish city is there an underground tube railway?

35 What was 'The Shetland Bus'?

36 What is the shortest sea route between Britain and Ireland?

37 Where is the lowest point at which the River Tay is spanned by a road bridge?

38 What is 'The Devil's Elbow'?

39 What Scottish packet boat was lost in the Irish Sea in 1953?

40 What is the String Road?

41 What was the name of the wartime port developed on the Gareloch?

42 'Pulling up Beattock, a steady climb,
The gradient's against her but she's on time . . .'
On what line was this railway train?

43 On the map opposite can you name:
A–F   Islands
G–L   Capes and headlands
M–R   Freshwater lochs
S–V   Sea lochs
W–Z   Towns

SCOTLAND

A' the Airts

1   What is a 'spaewife'?

2   From the lone shieling of the misty island
        Mountains divide us, and the waste of the seas—
    Yet still the blood is strong, the heart is Highland,
        And we in dreams behold the Hebrides.
    From what song are these lines taken?

3   What is a *wee deoch an doruis*?

4   What is the common Scots vernacular rendering of the motto,
        Nemo Me Impune Lacessit?

5   What is 'a lad o' pairts'?

6   What is the Swilcan?

7   Which is the observatory of the Astronomer Royal for Scotland?

8   What is Lallans?

9   Who is 'Wee Macgreegor'?

10 Of whom is 'The Immortal Memory'?

11 Which Scot wrote of *England Their England*?

12 What is 'The Curse of Scotland'?

13 Where are 'The Beech Hedges'?

14 Can you say who wrote the hymn, 'Abide with me'?

15 Where would you find Provand's Lordship, and what is it?

16 What is 'The Glasgow School'?

17 Where is the Well of the Heads and how does it get its name?

18 What is a box bed?

19 What is a 'garron'?

20 Which university had the first medical school in Britain?

21 Which Edinburgh citizen is supposed to have given R. L.
        Stevenson the model for his *Dr. Jekyll and Mr. Hyde*?

22 What would you be doing if you were kelp-gathering?

23 What are the *Book of Deer* and the *Book of Dean of Lismore*?

24 Which Scot wrote about a mole, a rat and a toad?

25 In what sphere was Sir Johnston Forbes Robertson famous?

26 Which famous actor of stage and screen has been Rector of the University of Edinburgh?

27 Which famous comedian has been Rector of the University of Aberdeen?

28 Which famous polar explorer has been Rector of the University of St. Andrews?

29 What is a blackface?

30 What is 'The Land o' Cakes'?

31 What is the Burrell Collection?

32 In what town would you find an annual ceremony involving the Burry Man, and how does he get his name?

33 Who was the Scottish 'hanging judge'?

34 Which royal jeweller founded a school?

35 Where do visitors knock pennies into a tree trunk and make their wish?

36 Can you name the only British subject who is allowed to keep a standing army?

37 Who was 'The Lady of Fotheringay'?

38 Can you give the last lines of these verses of well-known Scots nursery rhymes?

A Kitty Bairdie had a coo,
   Black and white about the mou',
   Wasna that a dainty coo?

B Dance tae yer daddie,
   My Bonnie laddie,
   Dance tae yer daddie,
   My bonnie lamb!
   Ye shall get a fishie,
   In a little dishie,
   Ye shall get a fishie,

C Hee baloo, my sweet wee Donald,
   Picture o' the great Clanronald,
   Thou'lt be chief o' all the clan,

Scotland's Past

Scotland's Past

1 Which famous battles occurred on these dates:
  A September, 1297   C September, 1513
  B June, 1314   D May, 1568

2 Which Scottish kings were called by these nicknames?
  A The Maiden
  B The Lion
  C Toom Tabard
  D The wisest fool in Christendom

3 How many Scottish kings bore each of the following names?
  A Malcolm   D James
  B David   E Charles
  C Robert

4 What was 'The First Book of Discipline'?

5 What was the 'Rough Wooing'?

6 What was 'The Black Dinner'?

7 Who was 'The Wolf of Badenoch'?

8 Where was it that a dead man won a fight?

9 What was 'The Auld Alliance'?

10 Which Scottish king was killed by being thrown from his horse on the cliffs of Fife?

11 Which Scottish queen lived in Hungary and in England before coming to Scotland?

12 What was the real name of Macbeth's wife?

13 Who founded the religious settlement on Iona?

14 What are cup and ring marks?

15 Who were 'The Seven Men of Moidart'?

16 What was the Battle of Mons Graupius?

17 What is the Antonine wall and between what points does it run?

18 Can you name the historical buildings on the opposite page?

Scotland's Past

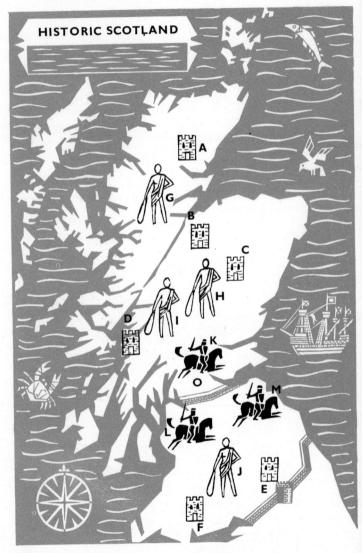

19 On the map opposite can you name the:
    A–F Castles G–J Old Scottish Kingdoms K–N Battles

20 Which Scottish king accomplished the conquest of the Hebrides?

21 Who was James Resby?

22 What was the name given to the Scottish nobles who banded together in 1557 to advance the Protestant cause?

23 For what is Catherine Douglas famed?

24 Which Scottish king married Margaret Tudor and paved the way for the union of the crowns?

25 What was the Darien Scheme?

26 Where were George Wishart and Patrick Hamilton burned?

27 What was 'Cleanse the Causeway'?

28 Who was Riccio or Rizzio?

29 What is Skara Brae?

30 What was *la garde ecossaise*?

31 When was the first Scottish Education Act?

32 Where was Darnley living at the time of his murder?

33 What was the Ruthven Raid?

34 What was the Solemn League and Covenant?

35 What was the National Covenant?

36 In which castle were the Honours of Scotland placed for protection after the Battle of Dunbar?

37 Where are the Honours of Scotland today?

38 Who was Bonnie Dundee?

39 What was the pre-Reformation archiepiscopal seat and ecclesiastical centre?

40 When was the Scottish Parliament united with the English Parliament?

41 Who was 'Bobbing John'?

42 Which battle in 1746 put an end to Charles Edward Stewart's hopes of the throne?

Scotland's Past

43 In what Scottish city would you have found the 'tobacco lords'?

44 There's some say that we wan,
Some say that they wan,
Some say that nane wan at a' . . .
Where?

45 What document was drawn up in 1320 to put to the Pope Scotland's case for independence in the face of the threat from England?

46 What are crannogs?

47 Which English king removed the Stone of Destiny from Scotland?

48 What is the Stone of Destiny and where is it to be found now?

49 Where was Robert the Bruce buried and where was his heart buried?

50 What is 'The Treasure of Traprain'?

51 What was the Candida Casa?

52 What is the meaning of the name, 'Canmore', applied to Malcolm III?

53 What are vitrified forts?

54 Which riot sprang from the death sentence passed on the two smugglers, Wilson and Robertson?

55 What were 'The Fifteen' and 'The Forty-Five'?

56 James IV built the largest ship of his time. Can you name it?

57 What was 'The Killing Time'?

58 Who were the Cameronians?

59 What was a conventicle?

60 Who was the maiden who swallowed men?

61 Which was the first Scottish colony?

62 Where was Mary Queen of Scots born?

Scottish Letters

1 Who wrote the following?

A *Catriona*
B *The Raiders*
C *Sunset Song*
D *John Splendid*
E *Morning Tide*
F *Sinister Street*
G *Peter Pan*
H *The House with the Green Shutters*
I *Humphry Clinker*
J *The Annals of the Parish*
K *The Shipbuilders*
L *The Mountain Lovers*
M *The Man of Feeling*
N *Coral Island*
O *Greenmantle*

2 In which of Scott's novels would you find the following characters:

A The Laird of Dumbiedykes
B Cuddie Headrigg
C Dandy Dinmont
D Peter Peebles
E Caleb Balderstone
F Conacher
G Rowena
H Bailie Duncan MacWheeble
I Snuffie Davie (Davie Wilson)
J Bailie Nicol Jarvie

3 Which Scottish writers are usually associated with the following places?

A Abbotsford
B Auchinleck
C Hawthornden
D Samoa
E Kyle

Scottish Letters

4 Which poets were the authors of these works:
   A *The Seasons*
   B *The Twa Dogs*
   C *The City of Dreadful Night*
   D *The Lay of the Last Minstrel*
   E *The Queen's Wake*
   F *The Testament of Cresseid*
   G *The Kingis Quair*
   H *The Battle of the Baltic*
   I *The Three Estates*
   J *The Bruce*

5 In which novels of Stevenson or Buchan do the following
      characters appear?
   A Captain Hoseason   D Mr. Henry
   B Scudder   E Laputa
   C Ben Gunn

6 Of which poems are these the opening lines? Where they are
      not anonymous, can you name the authors?

   A Day set on Norham's castled steep,
       And Tweed's fair river, broad and deep,
           And Cheviot's mountains lone: . . .
   B Faster than fairies, faster than witches,
       Bridges and houses, hedges and ditches; . . .
   C He cut a sappy sucker from the muckle rodden-tree,
       He trimmed it an' he wet it, an' he thumped it on
           his knee; . . .
   D On Linden, when the sun was low,
       All bloodless lay the untrodden snow. . . .
   E The king sits in Dunfermline toun
           Drinking the blude-red wine; . . .
   F It fell about the Martinmas time,
           And a gay time it was then,
       When our good wife got puddings to make,
           And boil'd them in the pan.
   G On the heights of Killiecrankie
           Yester-morn our army lay: . . .
   H True Thomas lay on Huntlie bank,
           A ferlie he spied with his e'e, . . .
   I When chapman billies leave the street,
       And drouthy neibors neibors meet, . . .

Scottish Letters

7 Which poets wrote the following poems on subjects of special interest to Scots?

   A *Yarrow Revisited*
   B *Inversnaid*
   C *An Ode on the Popular Superstitions of the Highlands of Scotland*
   D *Sonnet written upon the top of Ben Nevis*
   E *Epitaph on a Jacobite*
   F *English Bards and Scotch Reviewers*
   G *Flannan Isle*
   H *The Inchcape Rock*
   I *The Loss of the* Birkenhead
   J *The Burial of Sir John Moore after Corunna*

8 Can you identify these Scottish authors?

   A The Ettrick Shepherd   C Rantin', rovin' Robin
   B The Shirra   D The Herald-bard

9 Who asked the following questions:

   A O how can I your true love ken,
      Or how can I her know?
   B What became of your bloodhounds, my handsome young man?
   C Where sall we gang and dine today?
   D Is it not strange that, as ye sung,
      Seem'd in mine ear a death-peal rung,
      Such as in nunneries they toll
      For some departed sister's soul?
   E Will ye gang tae the Hielands, Lizzie Lindsay?

10 Which Scotsmen wrote the following notable books:

   A *The Golden Bough*
   B *The Life of Johnson*
   C *The Wealth of Nations*
   D *The French Revolution*
   E *An Enquiry Concerning Human Understanding*

11 Which Scottish authors used the following pen-names:

   A Fiona Macleod   D Christopher North
   B James Bridie   E Saki
   C Hugh M'Diarmid

12 Who wrote:

      'Wee Willie Winkie rins through the toun'?

Scottish Letters

13 From what poems by what authors are the following lines taken:

A Jack Elliot raised up his steel bonnet and lookit,
His hand grasped the sword with a nervous embrace:
   Ah, welcome, brave foemen,
   On earth there are no men
More gallant to meet in the foray or chase!

B This be the verse you grave for me:
Here he lies where he longed to be;
Home is the sailor, home from the sea,
   And the hunter home from the hill.

C Ah, Tam! gie me a Border burn
That canna rin without a turn,
And wi' its bonnie babble fills
The glens amang oor native hills.

D I gang like a ghaist, and carena to spin;
I darena think on Jamie, for that wad be a sin;
But I'll do my best a gude wife to be,
For oh! Robin Gray he is kind to me.

E Had we never loved sae kindly,
Had we never loved sae blindly,
Never met—or never parted,
We had ne'er been broken-hearted.

F I'm wearing awa', Jean,
Like snaw when it's thaw, Jean, . . .

G Phoebus, arise!
And paint the sable skies
With azure white, and red; . . .

H He is gone on the mountain,
   He is lost to the forest,
Like a summer-dried fountain,
   When our need was the sorest.

I Earl March look'd on his dying child,
   And, smit with grief to view her—
'The youth,' he cried, 'whom I exiled
   Shall be restored to woo her.'

14 Which Scottish authors wrote the following plays:

A *Sophonisba*   D *The Gentle Shepherd*
B *Tobias and the Angel*   E *The Admirable Crichton*
C *Douglas*

15 Can you identify the following famous literary dogs:
  A Bevis   D Mustard and Pepper
  B Luath   E Rab
  C Lufra   F Maida

16 Whose portraits are shown above?

17 Which is Scotland's smallest theatre?

18 What was Macpherson's *Ossian*?

19 What was the Kailyard School?

20 What was the jewel which inspired Scott's novel, *The Talisman*?

21 Who was William McGonagall?

22 Which early Scottish poet translated Virgil's *Aeneid* into Scots verse?

23 Leigh Hunt sang:
        Jenny kiss'd me when we met . . .
    Who was Jenny?

Scottish Letters

24 From which anonymous Scots poems are the following lines
taken:

  A The gypsies cam to our gude lord's yett,
      And wow but they sang sweetly;
   They sang sae sweet and sae very complete,
      That doun cam our fair lady.

  B Be a lassie e'er sae black,
      Gin she hae the name o' siller
   Set her upon Tintock tap,
      The wind will blaw a man till her.

  C He louted him o'er his saddle-bow,
      To kiss her cheek and chin;
   She's ta'en him in her arms twa,
      And thrown him headlong in.

  D 'Awa' wi' your former vows,' she says,
      'For they will breed but strife; . . .'

  E 'Blow up the fire, my maidens!
      Bring water from the well!
   For a' my house shall feast this night,
      Since my three sons are well.'

  F 'Oh who are ye, young man?' she said,
      'What country come ye frae?'
   'I flew across the sea,' he said,
      ''Twas but this very day.'

  G 'In ahint yon auld fail dyke,
   I wot there lies a new-slain knight;
   And naebody kens that he lies there
   But his hawk and his hound and his lady fair.'

  H When she came before the king,
      She knelit lowly on her knee:
   'O what's the matter, May Margaret?
      And what needs a' this courtesie?'

25 As I was walking all alone,
      Between a water and a wa'
   And there I spied a. . . . What?

26 Who was OH?

27 Can you name a Scottish poet who was an anthropologist,
a Greek scholar, an historian and a novelist?

Scottish Sport

1   Can you say in which towns the following association football
    teams have their home grounds?
    A St. Mirren   E Hibernians
    B St. Johnstone   F East Fife
    C Morton   G Queen of the South
    D Raith Rovers   H Third Lanark

2   With what sport are (or were) the following personalities
    associated:
    A James Braid   F Angus Cameron
    B Duncan Clark   G Ian Peebles
    C Willie Waddell   H Walter Donaldson
    D Pete Smith   I Jackie Paterson
    E Dunkie Wright   J Cathie Gibson

3   Which sports are associated with the following places:
    A Carsebreck Loch   E Loch Leven
    B Ibrox Stadium   F Gleneagles
    C Bogside   G Am Bhasteir
    D Murrayfield   H Raeburn Place

4   Can you identify the football teams popularly known by the
    following nicknames:
    A 'The Jags'   I 'The Honest Men'
    B 'The Bully Wee'   J 'The Dons'
    C 'The Sons of the Rock'   K 'The Steel Men'
    D 'The Loons'   L 'The Gable Endies'
    E 'The Spiders'   M 'The Bairns'
    F 'The Hi Hi'   N 'The Buddies'
    G 'The Pars'   O 'The Red Lichties'
    H 'The Doonhamers'

5   What is 'The Old Firm'?

6   When did the Ibrox disaster occur and what was it?

7   What Scottish football side plays on a ground that is named
    after another sport?

8   Which Scottish football side uses Hampden Park as its home
    ground?

Scottish Sport

9   What is the highest score recorded in a first class football match?

10   Which Scottish footballer holds the record for the award of International Championship caps?

11   What is the record football international attendance?

12   What is a 'guttie'?

13   Who was the youngest ever winner of the British Open Golf Championship?

14   What is 'The Eden'?

15   Where and when was the first British Open played?

16   Which is the oldest Scottish Golf Club?

17   Which golf club exercises jurisdiction over the rules of golf?

18   With what sport is J. C. Wardrop associated?

19   For what sport is the Craw's Nest Tassie awarded?

20   Which Scottish motor-racing team won the Le Mans 24-Hour Race in 1956?

21   When was the first Association Football International Match between England and Scotland and what was remarkable about the selection of the Scottish Team?

22   In what sport are brooms used?

23   What is 'The Clyde Fortnight'?

24   Which is the oldest archery group in Scotland?

25   What is a caber?

26   With what sport is the popingoe or popinjay of Kilwinning associated?

27   For what team sport are the Borders famous?

28   Which Scot won an Olympic gold medal in the 1956 Olympic Games in Melbourne?

29   What is 'the glorious Twelfth'?

30   What is the Calcutta Cup?

31   What is 'Glasgow's Epsom'?

32   In deerstalking, what is a 'royal'?

33   If you were at a bonspiel, what game would you be playing?

34   For what sport is the Camanachd Cup awarded?

Music and Dancing

1 Which two Highland dances are commonly executed, one following the other without a break?

2 What is a *pibroch*?

3 Who was Niel Gow?

4 What is a *clarsach*?

5 If you danced a *Gillie Chaluim* what equipment would you require?

6 What are *puirt-a-beul*?

7 What is the correct name of the Highland dancing step often known as the *pas de bas*?

8 What is a 'bothy ballad'?

9 Do you know which symphony was called by its composer 'The Scotch Symphony'?

10 What is a chanter?

11 There is an annual Scottish gathering called 'The Mod'. To what art is it devoted?

12 What is *Piob Mhor*?

13 For what is Mrs. Kennedy Fraser famous?

14 What was 'The Glasgow Orpheus'?

15 What is *Crimond*?

16 'Ye'll tak' the high road and I'll tak' the low road
And I'll be in Scotland afore ye . . .'
   What is 'the low road'?

17 Who wrote Annie Laurie—and did Annie marry the author?

18 Who was cursed with a gentle wife and cured her of her airs by thrashing his 'ain sheepskin'?

19 What is a *ceilidh*?

Music and Dancing

20 'I wish I were where Helen lies . . .'
    Where does she lie?

21 What is a *corronach*?

22 Which song is often known as 'The Scottish National Anthem'?

23 What is the 'Scots Snap'?

24 In what Scottish song would you bid farewell to your hosts but
    promise a return visit?

25 What is 'waulking' and why should this question be in a section
    dealing with music?

26 'By yon bonnie banks and by yon bonnie braes . . .'
    Where?

27 What do the initials, S.N.O., stand for?

28 What ballet is set in the slums of Glasgow?

29 Where is the Usher Hall?

30 Which Scots comedian is associated with the song,
    Roamin' in the Gloamin'?

31 Here are the opening lines of some well-known Scots songs.
    Can you give the titles commonly given to them?

    A Why weep ye by the tide, ladye?
       Why weep ye by the tide?
    B Maxwelton Braes are bonnie
    C To the Lairds of Convention 'twas Claverhouse spoke
    D Should auld acquaintance be forgot
    E And are ye sure the news is true?
       And are ye sure he's weel?
    F Fareweel to Lochaber, fareweel to my Jean
    G March, march, Ettrick and Teviotdale
    H Speed, bonnie boat, like a bird on the wing
    I Bonnie Charlie's now awa'
    J When trees did bud and fields were green,
       And broom bloomed fair to see
    K I've seen the smiling of fortune beguiling
    L Ye Hielands and ye Lawlands,
       O, whar ha'e ye been?
    M Gin a body meet a body

Famous Scots

1 With what inventions are the following Scots associated:
   A James Watt   E Dr. James Young
   B John Logie Baird   F John Boyd Dunlop
   C R. A. Watson-Watt   G Alexander Graham Bell
   D John L. Macadam   H Andrew Meikle

2 In what fields are the following contemporary Scots famous:
   A Moira Shearer   F Eric Linklater
   B Douglas Young   G F. Fraser Darling
   C Duncan Macrae   H Sir Hector Hetherington
   D Cedric Thorpe Davie   I George Young
   E Sir William Y. Darling   J Lord Bilsland

3 What contributions to science were made by the following
   Scotsmen:
   A Napier of Merchiston   C Sir Alexander Fleming
   B Sir James Young Simpson   D Sir Ronald Ross

4 Where would you find the birthplaces of these Scotsmen:
   A David Livingstone   D J. M. Barrie
   B Andrew Carnegie   E Thomas Carlyle
   C Mungo Park

5 In what fields were the following Scots prominent:
   A Sir Henry Raeburn   E Dr. Thomas Chalmers
   B Sir Malcolm Campbell   F Adam Smith
   C Mary Slessor   G Sir Alexander MacKenzie
   D David Octavius Hill   H Douglas, Earl Haig

6 Which Scotsman pioneered the Transatlantic telegraph cable,
   perfected the mariner's compass and invented an apparatus
   for sounding the ocean from a moving ship?

7 Can you name an American sailor and privateer who was born
   in Kirkcudbrightshire?

8 What famous shipwrecked mariner was born in Largo, Fife?

9 Which Scotsman wrote a standard Bible concordance?

10 Which famous Scot has been associated with the problem of
   world food shortage in the present century?

Famous Scots

11 Who were William and John Hunter?

12 Which famous Scottish physicist made significant contributions to the theory of electricity and to the kinetic theory of gases?

13 Which Scotsman became Controller-General of Finance to a French Government?

14 What Scottish king learnt a lesson from a spider?

15 Can you name the Scotsman who founded the Independent Labour Party?

16 Who lived in Lauder Ha'?

17 What is the name of the Scot who discovered the source of the Blue Nile?

18 What is the name of the famous organization founded in Glasgow in 1883 by Sir William Smith?

19 Who discovered the Victoria Falls and where are they?

20 Can you name a famous Scottish yachtsman who made his fortune in the grocery business?

21 How many Scots have been Prime Minister of Great Britain in the present century and what are their names?

22 Which Scottish novelist became Governor-General of Canada?

23 What office is held by Lord Rowallan?

24 Which Scottish explorer traced the course of the Niger River?

25 If you had a McTaggart and a McWhirter what would you have?

26 Which Glasgow-born emigrant founded a Canadian University which still bears his name?

27 Can you name the Scotsman who designed the old Southwark, the old Waterloo and London Bridges?

28 In what field was Sir David Young Cameron famous?

29 What was the name of Queen Victoria's faithful Scots servant?

30 Which Scot was instrumental in the building of the Canadian Pacific Railway?

31 Who was Charles Rennie Mackintosh?

32 Who was the Admirable Crichton?

Famous Scots

33 The word *dunce* is surprisingly derived from the name of a great medieval Scottish scholar. Who was he?

34 What great imperial office was held by the Marquis of Dalhousie?

35 Who was the first white man to cross Australia from south to north?

36 Who was William Kidd?

37 To whom are the following dying sayings attributed:
  A 'God bless you all, I feel myself again.'
  B 'Don't let the awkward squad fire over my grave.'
  C 'Scots, follow me!'
  D 'Now it is come.'
  E 'It cam' wi' a lass, and it will gang wi' a lass.'

38 Can you name the famous Scots in the illustration above?

Land of Scotland

1 Can you identify these Scottish towns:
   A The Capital of the Highlands
   B The Honest Toun
   C The Queen of the South
   D The Athens of the North
   E The Blue Toun
   F Thrums
   G The Granite City
   H The Lang Toun
   I The Charing Cross of the Highlands
   J The Fair City
2 Can you identify the buildings in the illustration on the opposite page?
3 Can you name the mountains in the illustration below?

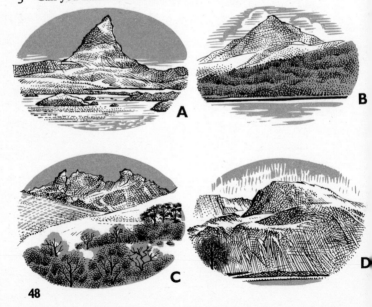

Land of Scotland

A

B

C

D

Land of Scotland

4 On what rivers do these towns stand:

A Stirling   F Kelso
B Aviemore   G Dumfries
C Perth   H Hawick
D Brechin   I Balmoral
E Lanark   J Blair Atholl

5 Do you know which are the county towns of these counties:

A Angus   E Ross and Cromarty
B Kincardine   F Berwick
C Argyll   G Caithness
D Moray   H Fife

6 Can you name the highest points in these counties:

A Dunbartonshire   D Inverness
B Fife   E Peebleshire
C Perthshire   F Stirlingshire

7 Which are the largest towns on these islands:

A Orkney   D Mull
B Skye   E Shetland
C Lewis

8 What are these natural features:

A Corrieshalloch   C Corra Linn
B Ailsa Craig   D Tinto

9 Can you identify these Scottish islands:

A An island with a memorial to four hundred American soldiers drowned when the *Tuscania* was torpedoed in 1918.
B An island off whose port a Spanish treasure ship was sunk.
C An island where a community is restoring a cathedral.
D A distant island which gives its name to a tiny bird.
E An island with an abbey in the River Forth.

10 On what lochs do these towns stand:

A Inverary   D St. Fillans
B Fort William   E Fort Augustus
C Killin

11 In what mountain ranges are the following peaks to be found:

A Braeriach   C Sgurr nan Gillean
B Goat Fell

Land of Scotland

12 Each of these places is dominated by a mountain for which its inhabitants feel a peculiar affection. Can you name the mountains:

A Fort William   B Tongue

13 Napoleon's first great defeat was in his retreat from Moscow and after his final downfall he was sent to St. Helena. Surprisingly enough there is a Moscow and a St. Helena in Scotland. Can you say where each is?

14 Which sands swallowed the granary of Moray?

15 How many counties are there in Scotland?

16 Which Scottish counties are composed entirely of islands?

17 Which is the largest county in Scotland?

18 Which is the smallest county?

19 Which is the most populous county?

20 Which county has the smallest population?

21 What is the most northerly point on the Scottish mainland?

22 Which is the longest river in Scotland?

23 Which is the largest island in Loch Lomond?

24 Which is the highest mountain in Scotland?

25 Which is the deepest freshwater loch?

26 Which is the largest freshwater loch?

27 Where are the highest cliffs in Scotland?

28 What is the most easterly point on the Scottish mainland?

29 Which is the largest island in the Hebrides?

30 Which is the largest city in Scotland?

31 Where is the Carse of Gowrie?

32 On what island would you find Fingal's Cave?

33 What formerly occupied the site of Princes Street Gardens, Edinburgh?

34 What are the better known names of these counties:

A Edinburghshire   C Haddingtonshire
B Linlithgowshire

35 Can you identify these vividly named natural features:
A The Devil's Beef Tub   B The Grey Mare's Tail

Land of Scotland

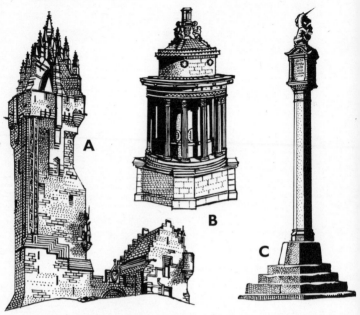

36 Which is the isle with the singing sands?

37 What and where are the monuments shown in the illustration above?

38 What is the most northerly habitation in the British Isles?

39 Where is Rob Roy's Cave?

40 What is the highest village in Scotland?

41 How many mountains in Scotland rise above 4,000 feet?

42 Where is Battery Hill?

43 Along what range of hills does the border between Scotland and England run?

44 What is the 'Linn of Dee'?

45 In what groups of islands are the following:

A Barra
B Stronsay
C Colonsay
D Yell

Robert Burns

1   Where was Burns born?

2   When is Burns Night?

3   After giving up farming, what occupation did Burns finally take up?

4   What two musical collections published in Burns lifetime contain songs contributed by Burns?

5   Can you give the name by which the first edition of the poems of Burns is known?

6   What was the title of this edition?

7   What is 'Mossgiel' and what connection has it got with Burns?

8   What was the maiden name of the wife of Burns?

9   What is 'Poosie Nancy's'?

10 Where is Burns' Cottage?

11 What is 'The Selkirk Grace'?

12 Each of the following extracts starts with the second line of a poem. Can you give the first line in each case:

A   Scots, wham Bruce has aften led,
    Welcome to your gory bed
        Or to victorie!

B   When we were first acquent,
    Your locks were like the raven,
        Your bonie brow was brent; . . .

C   'Bout vines, an' wines, an' drucken Bacchus, . . .

D   Ae farewell, and then forever!
    Deep in heart-wrung tears I'll pledge thee,
    Warring sighs and groans I'll wage thee.

E   That hings his head, an' a' that?
    The coward slave, we pass him by—
        We dare be poor for a' that!

F   Three kings both great and high,
    And they hae sworn a solemn oath
        John Barleycorn should die.

G   That's newly sprung in June.

Robert Burns

13 Each of the extracts below is the first verse of a song with a chorus. Can you give the chorus in each case:

A There's nought but care on ev'ry han',
    In every hour that passes, O:
What signifies the life o' man,
    An' twere na for the lasses, O.

B Hark, the mavis' e'ening sang
Sounding Clouden's woods amang,
Then a-faulding let us gang,
    My bonie dearie.

C Farewell, ye dungeons dark and strong,
    The wretches destinie!
MacPherson's time will not be long
    On yonder gallows-tree.

D Should auld acquaintance be forgot,
    And never brought to mind?
Should auld acquaintance be forgot,
    And days o' lang syne?

E Farewell to the Highlands, farewell to the North,
The birthplace of valour, the country of worth!
Wherever I wander, wherever I rove,
The hills of the Highlands for ever I love.

F But warily tent when ye come to court me,
    And come nae unless the back yett be a-jee;
Syne up the back-style, and let naebody see,
    And come as ye were na comin to me!

14 The following quotations are well known enough to be included in a standard dictionary of quotations. Can you say from which poems they are taken:

A Auld Ayr, wham ne'er a town surpasses,
For honest men and bonnie lasses.

B The fient a pride, nae pride had he.

C From scenes like these, old Scotia's grandeur springs,
    That makes her lov'd at home, rever'd abroad:
Princes and lords are but the breath of kings,
    'An honest man's the noblest work of God'; . . .

D Man's inhumanity to man
    Makes countless thousands mourn!

E But O, fell Death's untimely frost,
    That nipt my flower sae early!

[14] F Here some are thinkin on their sins,
      An' some upo' their claes; ...
  G Gie me ae spark o' Nature's fire,
      That 's a' the learning I desire;
      Then, tho' I drudge thro' dub an' mire
          At pleugh or cart,
      My Muse, tho' hamely in attire,
          May touch the heart.
  H And Ilka bird sang o' its luve,
      And fondly sae did I o' mine.

15 Burns had a habit of addressing people, animals or even inanimate things in his poems. Who was he addressing in the following?

  A Go live, poor wanderer of the wood and field,
      The bitter little that of life remains!
  B She prophesied, that late or soon,
      Thou would be found deep drowned in Doon, ...
  C Great is thy pow'r an' great thy fame;
      Far kend an' noted is thy name; ...
  D   All hail thy palaces and tow'rs,
      Where once, beneath a Monarch's feet,
        Sat Legislation's sov'reign pow'rs: ...
  E When first I gaed to woo my Jenny,
      Ye then was trotting wi' your minnie:
      Tho' ye was trickie, slee, an' funnie,
      Ye ne'er was donsie; ...
  F The groaning trencher there ye fill,
      Your hurdies like a distant hill,
      Your pin wad help to mend a mill
         In time o' need, ...
  G Wee, sleekit, cowrin, tim'rous beastie,
      O, what a panic's in thy breastie!

16 Here are two famous passages from Burns. Can you say what poems they are taken from?

  A The best laid schemes o' mice an' men
      Gang aft agley, ...
  B O wad some Power the giftie gie us
      To see oorsels as ithers see us!

17 Where is Burns buried?

Scotland at Work

1 Can you rearrange the following list to associated each product
   with its most appropriate place:

A	Jute	Alloa
B	Linoleum	Greenock
C	Shawls	Dunfermline
D	Tweed	Clydebank
E	Knitwear	Kirkcaldy
F	Silk	Fort William
G	Sugar	Harris
H	Aluminium	Hawick
I	Glass bottles	Paisley
J	Ships	Dundee

2 What were the colours of the old Scots dyes extracted from these
   plants?

   A Broan   C Elderberry
   B Dock root   D Rue root

3 What is the largest ship ever built on the Clyde?

4 What is the link between Dundee and Calcutta?

5 What are the meanings of the following words, all of which
   might be heard in a discussion of Highland crofting:

   A A caschrom   B Quoils   C Lazybeds

6 What great industrial experiment took place in New Lanark?

7 Why should Dundee have become a great centre of jam-making
   and canning?

8 What is a steading?

9 Which industry is associated with the family of Coats and
   which with the family of Dewar?

10 Which island in the Shetlands is famous for knitwear of
   complicated patterns?

11 Can you name the Clyde-built ships shown opposite?

Scotland at Work

Scotland at Work

12 What is 'a Cheviot lion'?

13 If you decided to build in Rubislaw, what would be your
    intention?

14 What is a 'knappin'-hammer'?

15 What industry is recalled in the name Prestonpans?

16 What is a carronade?

17 What was run-rig?

18 Which are the note-issuing banks in Scotland?

19 Why is Aberdeen a suitable centre for paper-making?

20 For what is Douneray in Caithness famous?

21 As one passes along many glens in the Highlands one finds
    great camps set up by civil engineering contractors. What
    are these contractors working on in these remote areas?

22 For what textile product are Darvel and Newmilns famous?

23 What minor industry do Carnoustie and St. Andrews share
    and why did it grow up in these places?

24 What sea-going industry did Dundee and Peterhead formerly
    have in common?

25 Four famous breeds of cattle are shown opposite. Can you name
    them?

26 Arran Banner, Great Scot, Edzell Blue, Craig's Defiance,
    Dunbar Cavalier. What are these?

27 What Scottish city is associated with the printing of boys'
    adventure stories, comics and family weekly magazines?

28 What do the street names, Jamaica Street and Tobago Street
    tell us of Glasgow's history?

29 On what port is Scotland's largest trawler fleet based?

30 Who were Robert and Andrew Foulis?

31 Why did Glasgow become early associated with the tobacco
    trade?

A

B

C

D

Traditions of the Highlands and Islands

1   What is Rory Mor's Drinking Horn?
2   Where is Rob Roy's grave?
3   With what art are the MacCrimmons associated?
4   What is a fiery cross?
5   Which is the nameless clan?
6   What is a kelpie?
7   Where is the festival of Up-Helly-Aa celebrated and what does it mark?
8   What are trows?
9   Can you name a Lerwick schoolmaster who emigrated and became the premier of New Zealand?
10 What is the Brooch of Lorne and where is it to be found today?
11 For what island are two missionaries said to have raced, what were their names and by what trick did the winner gain his victory?
12 Which Hebridean island is so flat as to have earned the name *An Rioghachd Barr fo Thuinn*, The Kingdom whose Summits lie beneath the Waves?
13 Which is Pig Island?
14 On what island would you find Compass Hill and how does it get its name?
15 In what cave were almost four hundred of the inhabitants of Eigg suffocated and by whom?
16 What is the Faery Flag of the McLeods and what power is attributed to it?
17 What is Rory Mor's nurse?
18 Who was Donald of Islay?
19 What is a banshee?

60

Traditions of the Highlands and Islands

20   Which Shetlander was called before the King of Norway for killing his tax collector and won his own life by capturing a bear?

21   Why was it the King of Norway before whom he was called?

22   Why is a horseshoe sometimes put in an infant's cradle?

23   Where would you find the Reliquary of St. Columba and what was its purpose supposed to have been?

24   What remarkable local attraction brings many tourists to Inverewe?

25   Who was 'The Glendale Martyr'?

26   What is a *birlinn*?

27   What is Cluny's Cage and who was its most famous occupant?

28   Where would you find a Soldier's Leap across the Tay?

29   What tradition is associated with the cup of St. Magnus?

30   Who was Duncan Bàn Macintyre?

31   What are 'the merry dancers'?

32   Where is 'The Shetlanders' Fjord'?

33   Where would you find a cathedral dedicated to St. Magnus?

34   What is the Clan Chattan?

35   What was the Althing of Orkney?

36   Who owns the present earldom estates of Orkney?

37   What is the name for the inhabitants of Orkney?

38   Which famous Earl of Orkney perished from a dead man's bite?

39   What is 'The Old Man of Hoy'?

40   When could many highlanders have had £30,000 for the asking yet would not take it?

41   Of which clan is Lochiel the chief?

42   Who was massacred in Glencoe?

43   Which famous Scotswoman assisted Prince Charles Edward Stewart in his flight?

Speirin' Loons

These questions have been provided by schoolchildren

1   What does 'speiring' mean?
2   Which two towns are situated at either end of the Caledonian Canal?
3   What is the name of the loch formed by damming at Pitlochry?
4   Apart from the Great Glen, not really a glen at all, what is the longest glen in Scotland?
5   Where is Barrowland?
6   What was the capital of Scotland in the time of Malcolm Canmore?
7   What is the name of the park in which the Braemar Gathering is held?
8   Where was the first H.M.S. *Vanguard* sunk?
9   What is a 'cleg'?
10 By whom was *The Grey Coast* written?
11 What art does Sydney Goodsir Smith practise?
12 *The House with the Green Shutters* has the same basic theme as one of the novels of A. J. Cronin. Which novel?
13 What is the area of Scotland?
14 What is the population of Scotland?
15 How many members does Scotland send to Parliament?
16 When was the *Scotsman* newspaper established?
17 How did the Black Watch get its name?
18 Where is the cave where Bruce is reputed to have seen the spider?
19 What are Flodden Wall and Telfer's Wall?
20 Name two books by Neil M. Gunn whose title includes the word *well*.
21 The birds on the opposite page can all be found in Scotland. Can you name them?

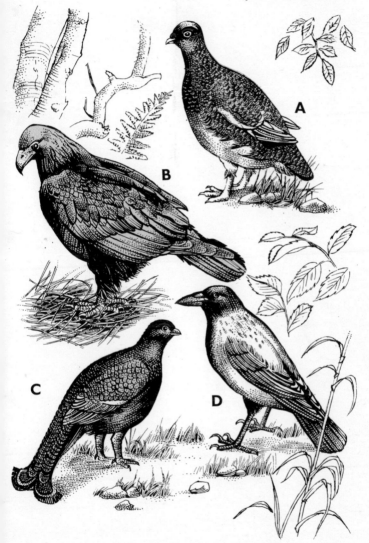

Speirin' Loons

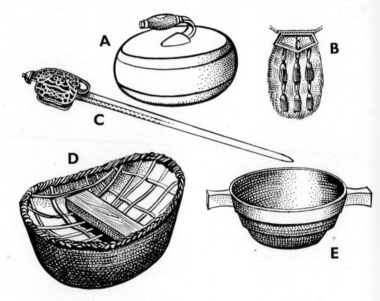

22 What are the objects shown in the illustration above?

23 What is 'a guid willie waucht'?

24 When was the last time a native Scot, living in Scotland, won the Open Golf Championship and what was his name?

25 How many cities in Scotland have a Lord Provost? Can you name them?

26 Where is the source of the Aberdeenshire Dee?

27 Which of the following is farthest north: Loch Awe, Loch Rannoch, Loch Tay, Loch Earn?

28 Which football team was champion of the Scottish League in the first year of the League's existence?

29 Which loch has eleven islands, eleven rivers feeding it and is eleven miles round?

30 What is the name of the Queen's Bodyguard in Scotland?

31 Where is the Ridge of Kings?

32 Can you name nine firths which are completely within the Scottish border?

33 What do the initials S.Y.H.A. stand for?

34 Who publishes the standard climbing guides to the Highlands of Scotland?

35 What is Athol Brose?

36 Which clan has a wild boar's head in its crest?

37 What are 'Buchan's cold spells'?

38 How many Stewartries are there in Scotland and what are they?

39 Which Scottish king 'raided the raiders' in the Borders?

40 What is 'barley bree'?

41 Who wrote the standard life of Sir Walter Scott?

42 What are the rhinns of Galloway?

43 Which is 'The Glen of Weeping'?

44 What was Black Friday?

45 What do we mean when we say that a horse turns 'widdershins' and what does it mean if it does so after you have just mounted it?

46 What is a corrie?

47 The Prologue to Pope's Satires is dedicated to a Scotsman who was a wit of his day and a friend of Pope. Who was he?

48 Where would you find 'John Knox's House'?

49 When is Johnsmas?

50 Where did the Maid of Norway die?

51 Where was the Stone of Destiny before it was taken to Scone by Kenneth II?

52 'Dinna fash yersel" means what?

Finding Things Out in Scotland

1 Where would you look if you wished to locate a portrait of a famous Scot of the past?

2 Where would you look up the meaning of a Scots word?

3 Which library exists for the purpose of lending to Scottish libraries books for serious students which they cannot supply from stock?

4 Which dictionary published by a Scottish firm is generally accepted as the standard crossword puzzle dictionary?

5 Which Scot edited the English dictionary which is accepted as the standard authority on English words and what dictionary is this?

6 Which is the only Scottish copyright library?

7 By whom is the standard reference work on *The Surnames of Scotland* published?

8 How many Scottish volumes of the telephone directory are published by the G.P.O.?

9 Where could you find out the assessed rental of a house?

10 Where would you find a Scottish will?

11 By whom is *Munro's Tables* published?

12 Where could you find details of the ancient monuments of Scotland?

13 How could you find out if you are qualified to enter a Scottish university?

14 Which body devotes itself to providing cheap accommodation for young people touring Scotland on foot or by cycle?

15 Where would you find the name of the Member of Parliament for your constituency?

ANSWERS

Scotch Broth

1 The streets leading from Holyrood Palace to Edinburgh Castle: Canongate, High Street, Lawnmarket, Castlehill, Castle Esplanade

2 1,984 yards

3 A mountain included in Munro's Tables of the mountains of Scotland over 3,000 feet

4 Resurrection men or body snatchers in Edinburgh in the early nineteenth century

5 Holy Cross

6 Dunbartonshire. The town is spelt with an *m*, the county with an *n*

7 An island in the Firth of Clyde between the Ayrshire coast and the Island of Bute

8 Twelve

9 The Tay Bridge disaster

10 The 'dead' shell erected as a collecting box after the First World War in Central Station, Glasgow, and famous as a place of rendezvous

11 St. Andrews, 1411, Glasgow, 1451, Aberdeen, 1494, Edinburgh, 1582

12 Forfar bridies, Loch Fyne kippers or herring, Edinburgh rock, Dundee cake, Selkirk bannock, Arbroath smokies, Dunlop cheese

13 The shore of Loch Ness near the point at which he lost his life while attempting to break the world's water speed record

14 A sheep's lights, liver and heart, beef suet, onions, oatmeal, the whole seasoned with salt and black pepper and cooked in a sheep's stomach

15 Down the Clyde, usually at one of the holiday resorts favoured by the citizens of Glasgow

16 The capture of Portobello by Admiral Vernon in 1739

17 A small village

18 St. Andrews University

19 A series of artificially stepped pools which enable salmon to by-pass a dam. There is a famous one at Pitlochry

20 St. Andrew

21 St. Kentigern, also called St. Mungo

Scotch Broth

22 Old Scots coinage

23 Fortingall, Perthshire

24 St. Margaret's Chapel in Edinburgh Castle, *circa* 1090

25 A In the Cairngorms

   B The Old Course, St. Andrews

26 Old Scotland Yard occupied the site of an old palace belonging to the King of Scotland and the name was transferred to New Scotland Yard

27 A famous old cannon in Edinburgh Castle

28 A Dutchman, John de Groot, is said to have had a house there, octagonal in shape and with a door in each side, so that the eight branches of his family should not quarrel over precedence

29 Orkney, off which Kitchener was drowned

30 The Crown (except in Orkney and Shetland where some is privately owned)

31 The Fortingall Yew, Perthshire

32 The collection of classical sculptures assembled by the seventh Earl of Elgin and now in the British Museum

33 Two. The Lake of Mentieth and Pressmennan Lake, East Lothian, the latter formed by damming

34 David Allan, the artist

35 Mendelssohn

36 1890

37 The thistle

38 The Devil

39 About three pints imperial measure

40 Culzean Castle, Ayrshire

41 1938, Bellahouston Park

42 Pheasant, Grouse, Partridge in descending order

43 A Edinburgh University
   B Glasgow
   C Dumbarton
   D St. Andrews
   E Inverness
   F Aberdeen University

44 Glasgow Art Galleries

45 The old measures which were adopted as Scottish standards

46 Subject of a celebrated trial in Glasgow. She was tried for the murder of Pierre L'Angelier in 1857 and the verdict was 'Not Proven'

47 A famous fictional skipper of a small Clyde and West Coast cargo steamer. He was created by Neil Munro

48 Rothiemurchus, in the Cairngorms. It has been brought into Scotland as an experiment

49 Rockall

50 Schiehallion

Scottish Life

1. A Edinburgh
   B Dundee
   C St. Andrews
   D Glasgow
   E Troon
   F Kirriemuir
   G Cupar, Fife
   H Aberdeen
   I Crieff
   J Stornoway

2. A Aberdeen
   B Edinburgh
   C Glasgow
   D Dundee
   E Glasgow

3. A Inveraray Castle
   B Dunvegan Castle, Skye
   C Glamis Castle
   D Floors Castle
   E Dunrobin Castle

4. A Edinburgh
   B Stirling
   C Inverness
   D Balmoral

5. A Teachers' Training College in Glasgow
   B Technical College in Edinburgh
   C Physical training (women)

6. A 31st December
   B 31st October
   C 30th November
   D 1st August

7. A Aberdeen
   B Glasgow
   C Edinburgh

8. The Kelvingrove Art Gallery

9. The Kelvin Hall, Glasgow

10. The Assessed Rental

11. The Assembly Hall, The Mound, Edinburgh

12. The annual conference and assembly of the Church of Scotland

13. Edinburgh Castle

14. The Lord Advocate

15. The Lord Justice General

16. The Lord President of the Court of Session

17. Not proven

18. Sheriff-Substitute

19. Perth Academy (1761)

20. Glasgow

21. A mid-term university holiday, originally to allow poor students to return home to replenish their stocks of oatmeal

22. *The Aberdeen Journal* (founded 1746), now *The Aberdeen Press and Journal*

23. The engineer

24. The extensive bridge where Glasgow Central Station crosses Argyle Street and affords ample shelter

25. A magistrate who is second in rank in a royal burgh, equivalent to an English alderman (also a farm steward)

26. A children's game

Scottish Life

27 As soon after midnight on 31st December as he could get there: he is the first to cross your threshold in the new year

28 The first Monday of the new year

29 The top pupil of a school

30 Originally a Highland chief's personal servant, now usually one who attends on sportsmen in shooting or fishing

31 Hallowe'en

32 To look up the time of a train

33 A famous character on the Scottish Children's Hour

34 The election of the students' representative on the University Court, the Rector

35 St. Andrews House

36 Repertory theatres in Glasgow and Edinburgh respectively

37 The annual payment in perpetuity of rent to a land superior for land held

38 A famous Scottish strip cartoon family

A Guid Scots Tongue

1 A A kilt
   B A dirk stuck in the stocking
   C The pouch hung in front of the kilt
   D A shoe

2 A A yearling ox or cow
   B A caterpillar
   C A daddy long legs
   D A polecat
   E A salmon trout
   F A ladybird
   G An earwig
   H A frog
   I A sparrow
   J The ant

3 A You would be keeping silent or keeping calm
   B Going warily or working slowly in an industrial dispute
   C Paying attention, taking notice
   D Making sure

4 A The Devil's sixpence, given in exchange for a man's soul
   B One who has failed to qualify as a minister of the church
   C A wall clock with a free-swinging pendulum
   D A sailor
   E The Moon
   F A Jew's harp
   G A shilling
   H A scarecrow
   I A short chemise
   J A turkey
   K An organ
   L A top-hat
   M A native of Peterhead
   N A small pebble
   O A potato lifter
   P A small squire
   Q A salt herring
   R A daughter-in-law
   S A large whisky jar

A Guid Scots Tongue

[4] T A highland sword with a basket hilt

U An eccentric, conspicuous person

V A loaf which is easy to cut since it is not too fresh

W Buckles or ties round the trousers just below the knees, commonly worn by labourers

X A fair Friday in a period of bad weather, said to indicate more rain

Y Reheated broth, hence an old sermon served up anew, an old love affair rekindled, etc.

Z Pennies thrown to children at weddings

5 A Unearthly, weird, ghostly
B Mocking
C Puffed, panting
D Foaming, overflowing
E Tedious, dreary
F Agreeable, snug, comfortable
G Growling, stormy, rough
H Smooth, sly
I Tasteless, insipid
J Worn out, exhausted

6 In the parlour at the back of the house

7 A Fussy, fastidious
B Ugly
C Large-mouthed, talkative
D Cross-grained, stubborn
E Senseless, affected
F Self-willed, contrary
G Plump, jolly, lucky
H Long-nosed
I Thirsty, drunken
J Shrewd, sly
K Left-handed

[7] L Docile, easily led
M Kind, sober-minded, respectable, soothing
N Fat, inactive, stupid
O Morose and taciturn
P Slender
Q Feeble, tasteless, weak-minded
R Enchanted, acting as if under a doom
S Stern, sullen, uncommunicative
T Making great profession of piety, excessively strait-laced

8 A Sheep's head broth
B Soup based on fowl boiled with leeks
C Thin broth made of water, barley and greens
D Crab soup
E Mashed potatoes
F Mixture of raw oatmeal and water

9 A Points of the compass, directions
B Foolish talk, nonsense
C The 'ridges' of growing corn
D Whims, caprices, fancies
E Scandalous tales, silly talk
F Fripperies, articles of adornment
G Ornamental china dogs
H Lasses and lads
I Fascinations, witchcraft
J Pedlar fellows
K Whisky
L Labourers on farms who do odd jobs rather than any particular assignment

A Guid Scots Tongue

[9] M Highland robbers or freebooters

N Mists sweeping in from the sea on the east coast

O Schoolmasters

P Pieces of food eaten immediately after bathing

Q Slices of bread, packed lunches

R Flint arrowheads

S Bad fiddlers

T Vagrants who sleep in the common stairs of tenement buildings

10 A Arbroath
B Hamilton
C Jedburgh
D St. Andrews

11 A nickname or an additional name given in a village or district where many have exactly the same name, so that similarly named people may be distinguished. Often the birth certificate name is hardly used at all, even for official and postal purposes

12 The bristly country

13 Your little finger

14 Lift the latch

15 Upside down, topsy turvy

16 A hundred thousand welcomes

17 A haaflin is a half-grown boy

Scotland in Arms

1 The Royal Scots

2 A The Black Watch
B The Cameronians
C The Scots Greys

3 A The Royal Scots
B The Royal Scots Fusiliers
C The Seaforth Highlanders
D The Highland Light Infantry (The City of Glasgow Regiment)
E The Argyll and Sutherland Highlanders

4 The Black Watch (1739)

5 Detachments from Scottish regiments were on board and stood in parade order on deck while the ship sank under them, in order that the women and

[5] children might be saved. Not a single woman or child was lost: almost all the soldiers lost their lives

6 The Royal Scots. Queen Victoria's father, the Duke of Kent, was colonel of the regiment at the time of her birth

7 A The Hunting Stewart
B The 42nd (Black Watch) tartan
C The Gordon Tartan

8 They were formations based on the emigrant Scots who are a substantial element in all the Commonwealth populations

73

Scotland in Arms

Traditions of the Borders and Lowlands

Traditions of the Borders and Lowlands

16 That of Archbishop Sharp of St. Andrews, murdered there 3rd May, 1679

17 Battle of Chevy Chase

18 Mary Hamilton

19 A laird who lived beside the Esk and attained an immortality by being satirized as a wooer by Lady Nairne

20 The land between the Esk and Sark on the Borders of England and Scotland, not firmly held by either country but 'debateable'

21 Galashiels

22 Hawick

23 Selkirk

24 From its use by Margaret, wife of Malcolm Canmore

25 Margaret MacLachlan and Margaret Wilson, killed for their religion by drowning at stakes set in the Solway Firth

26 St. Cyrus, Kincardineshire

27 Biggar's Biggar

28 Scott's servant, originally a poacher who appeared before Scott in his capacity as sheriff and whose fine Scott paid

29 Sweetheart Abbey

30 The Old Tolbooth of Edinburgh (Lucken—locked)

31 The woman traditionally reputed to have thrown a stool at Dean Hannay when he read the new liturgy in St. Giles in 1637

32 The hill which overlooks Edinburgh

33 A famous and beautifully ornamented Celtic stone cross (Ruthwell, Dumfriesshire)

34 St. Andrews Castle

35 Loch Leven Castle, Fife

36 The Heir o' Linne

37 Robert Bruce

38 Thomas the Rhymer, also known as True Thomas.

39 Huntly Bank

40 Yarrow

Transport and Communications

1 A Loch Leven (Sea Loch)
   B River Forth
   C Loch Carron
   D Beauly Firth
   E River Clyde

2 A Edinburgh and London
   B Glasgow, Edinburgh and Leeds

[2] C Glasgow, Edinburgh and London
    D Glasgow and St. Andrews
    E London and Aberdeen

3 A Edinburgh
   B Paisley
   C Glasgow
   D Dundee
   E Glasgow

Transport and Communications

4 A Turnhouse
   B Sumburgh
   C Dalcross
   D Renfrew and Prestwick
   E Dyce

5 A Caledonian Railway
   B Great North of Scotland
     Railway
   C Glasgow and South
     Western Railway
   D North British Railway
   E Highland Railway

6 A Cloch Point, Firth of Clyde,
     Renfrewshire bank
     opposite Dunoon
   B St. Abb's Head, north of
     Eyemouth, Berwickshire
   C Firth of Forth off North
     Berwick
   D Southern point of approach
     to Aberdeen harbour
   E Off Firth of Tay, eleven
     miles out to sea south-
     east of Arbroath

7 A The Forth Bridge
   B General Wade's Bridge
     across the Tay at Aber-
     feldy
   C The Tay Bridge
   D The old Stirling Bridge

8 A The Road to the Isles
   B Tam o' Shanter's Ride
   C Charles Edward's advance,
     1745

9 A Tay Bridge
   B Forth Bridge
   C Kincardine Swing Bridge

10 A Leith
   B Glasgow
   C Thurso

11 The Royal Border Bridge

12 A great pass in the Cairngorms between Rothie-
   murchus and the upper
   Dee

13 The Kilmarnock and Troon
   Railway (1808)

14. The Monkland and Kirk-
   intilloch Railway

15 Five. The Caledonian, the
   Crinan, the Forth and
   Clyde, the Edinburgh
   and Glasgow Union, the
   Monkland, the last no
   longer navigable

16 One of the small cargo
   steamers plying in the
   Clyde and up the west
   coast

17 Greenock Tunnel (1 mile,
   340 yards)

18 The Clyde

19 Posts erected alongside a road
   to show its course when
   the snow obliterates it

20 The series of locks at the
   west end of the Caledonian
   Canal

21 Thurso

22 Famous Clyde steamers

23 Druimauchdar Pass, 1,484 ft.

24 Drove roads are roads by
   which cattle or sheep were
   formerly driven across
   country to market: Wade's
   roads are those built by
   General Wade in his cam-
   paign to subdue the Scots
   Jacobites (18th cent.)

25 A neck of land across which
   boats may be dragged, a
   portage

Transport and Communications

26 The pass of Glen Croe, Argyll, the summit of which is marked by a stone so inscribed (also a point in Midlothian giving a remarkable view of Edinburgh)

27 The Albion Commercial Motor

28 Loch Lochy, Loch Oich, Loch Ness. Loch Dochfour is sometimes considered as part of Loch Ness. Entrance at Western end from sea loch, Loch Linnhe

29 A93 Blairgowrie-Braemar road at Cairnwell Pass (2,199 ft.)

30 *The Comet*

31 Both pairs are linked by bridges over the Atlantic Ocean

32 The Prestwick Pioneer

33 They are both television transmitting stations of the B.B.C.

34 Glasgow

35 The fishing boats which, plying between Shetland and Norway during the war, provided a link with the Norwegian underground movement

36 Stranraer to Larne

37 Perth

38 A notorious hairpin bend on the Blairgowrie–Braemar road (A 93)

39 T.S.M.V. *Princess Victoria*

40 The road from Brodick to Blackwaterfoot in Arran, like a string round the waist of the island

41 Faslane

42 The main line north from Carlisle where it crosses Beattock Moor from Dumfrieshire into Lanarkshire. The poem is *Night Mail* by W. H. Auden and was used as the sound track for a film. Have you read it?

43 A Orkney
    B Lewis
    C Skye
    D Mull
    E Islay
    F Arran
    G Fife Ness
    H Duncansby Head
    I Cape Wrath
    J Butt of Lewis
    K Mull of Kintyre
    L Turnberry Point
    M Shin
    N Ness
    O Shiel
    P Tay
    Q Awe
    R Leven
    S Broom
    T Carron
    U Linnhe
    V Fyne
    W Inverness
    X Montrose
    Y Rothesay
    Z Stranraer

A' the Airts

1 A fortune teller

2 *The Canadian Boatsong*

3 A stirrup cup, a parting cup

4 Wha daur meddle wi' me

5 A boy of intellectual ability

6 A famous burn crossing the first and eighteenth fairways of the Old Course, St. Andrews

7 The Royal Observatory, Edinburgh

8 Lowland Scots as written by many modern Scottish authors

9 A literary character created by J. J. Bell

10 Robert Burns

11 A. G. MacDonnell

12 The nine of diamonds—there are various explanations of the origin of this phrase

13 Meikleour, Perthshire

14 H. Francis Lyte

15 Glasgow, where it is the only surviving pre-Reformation dwelling-house

16 A group of artists working in Glasgow in the late nineteenth century. Sir John Lavery and E. A. Hornel are perhaps the best known

17 A well on the west shore of Loch Oich. Seven men's heads are carved round it in stone: seven brothers murdered their nephews

18 An enclosed bed made of wood, usually with wooden doors, and formerly used extensively by cottagers

19 A strong Highland pony

20 Aberdeen (1505)

21 William Brodie, town councillor and respected citizen by day and criminal by night

22 Gathering seaweed

23 Early Gaelic chronicles

24 Kenneth Grahame

25 He was an actor

26 Alastair Sim

27 Jimmy Edwards

28 Nansen

29 A breed of sheep, the commonest in the Highlands

30 Scotland

31 A large collection of pictures and *objets d'art* gifted to Glasgow by Sir William Burrell

32 South Queensferry. He is covered with burrs

33 Lord Braxfield (1722–99)

34 George Heriot

35 The Holy Tree, Loch Maree

36 The Duke of Atholl (The Atholl Highlanders)

37 Mary Queen of Scots

38 A Dance Kitty Bairdie
B When the boat comes in
C If thou'rt spared to be a man

Scotland's Past

1
- A Battle of Stirling Bridge
- B Battle of Bannockburn
- C Battle of Flodden
- D Battle of Langside

2
- A Malcolm IV (1153–65)
- B William (1165–1214)
- C John Balliol (1292–96)
- D James VI (I of England) (1567–1625)

3
- A Four
- B Two
- C Three
- D Seven (James VII also James II of England)
- E Two (Charles II also Charles II of England)

4 A plan for the new Protestant Church drawn up by Knox and others

5 Henry VIII's attacks on Scotland to secure a marriage for the Prince of Wales with the Scottish Queen, Mary

6 A bull's head served at dinner, a sign that someone present was to be put to death, when Livingstone and Crighton seized William, sixth Earl of Douglas, whom they subsequently caused to be executed

7 Alexander, Earl of Buchan, brother of Robert III

8 This is said of Douglas at the Battle of Otterburn

9 The alliance of Scotland and France usually held to date from 1295

10 Alexander III

11 Margaret, wife of Malcolm Canmore

12 Gruoch

13 St. Columba

14 Prehistoric markings in rock often found in graves

15 The seven companions who sailed to Scotland with Prince Charles Edward Stewart in 1745

16 Battle between Agricola and the Caledonians who were ultimately defeated

17 The Roman wall built across Mid-Scotland running from Old Kilpatrick to Carriden-on-Forth

18
- A Broch of Mousa, Berwick
- B Linlithgow Palace
- C Hermitage Castle
- D Eileen Donnan Castle

19
- A Dunrobin
- B Inverness
- C Balmoral
- D Barcaldine
- E Hermitage
- F Kirkudbright
- G Northern Picts
- H Southern Picts
- I Scots
- J Angles
- K Bannockburn
- L Largs
- M Dunbar

20 Alexander III

Scotland's Past

21 A martyr burned in Perth, 1407, and often claimed to be the first Scottish martyr in the Protestant cause

22 The Lords of the Congregation

23 Using her arm as a bolt to bar the door against James I's murderers: her arm was broken. She is often called Kate Barlass

24 James IV

25 An unsuccessful scheme to found a Scottish colony in Darien, isthmus of Panama

26 St. Andrews

27 A battle in Edinburgh in which the Douglases defeated the Hamiltons (1520)

28 Secretary to Mary Queen of Scots. He was murdered by several noblemen including Darnley, Mary's husband

29 A beautifully preserved Stone Age village in Orkney

30 The French king's Scots guard

31 1496

32 Kirk o' Field, Edinburgh

33 The seizure of James VI in 1582 by Gowrie and other noblemen and his confinement in Ruthven Castle

34 1643 Treaty between the Covenanters and the English Parliamentary forces in which the Covenanters agreed to help Parliament against Charles I in return for a Presbyterian régime in both England and Scotland

35 A covenant signed in protest against the Roman Catholic religion, 1638

36 Dunnottar, Kincardineshire

37 Edinburgh Castle

38 John Graham of Claverhouse, Viscount Dundee

39 St. Andrews

40 1707

41 John, Earl of Mar, famous for changing sides. He voted for Act of Union and then supported Charles Edward

42 Battle of Culloden

43 Glasgow

44 The Battle of Sheriffmuir

45 The Declaration of Arbroath

46 Prehistoric lake dwellings

47 Edward I

48 The Stone on which the Scottish Kings were formerly crowned. Now beneath the seat of the Coronation Chair in Westminster Abbey

49 A Dunfermline Abbey
   B Melrose Abbey

Scotland's Past

50 A hoard of silver ornaments and Roman coins discovered on Traprain Law, East Lothian

51 The White church of St. Ninian at Whithorn

52 Bighead

53 Ancient Forts, the stones of which are fused by burning

54 The Porteous Riot. It is dealt with in Scott's *Heart of Midlothian*

55 The risings against the Hanoverians in favour of James Edward and Charles Edward Stewart respectively

56 *The Great Michael*

57 A period of persecution of Cameronians and others, 1684–5

58 An extremist Protestant group called after Richard Cameron, who led a movement of religious revolt against Charles II

59 An illegal religious meeting, especially of the Covenanters

60 The Scottish Guillotine

61 Nova Scotia, 1629

62 Linlithgow Palace

Scottish Letters

1 A Robert Louis Stevenson
B S. R. Crockett
C Lewis Grassic Gibbon
D Neil Munro
E Neil Gunn
F Compton Mackenzie
G J. M. Barrie
H George Douglas Brown
I Tobias Smollett
J John Galt
K George Blake
L Fiona Macleod
M Henry Mackenzie
N R. M. Ballantyne
O John Buchan

2 A *The Heart of Midlothian*
B *Old Mortality*
C *Guy Mannering*
D *Redgauntlet*
E *The Bride of Lammermoor*

[2] F *The Fair Maid of Perth*
G *Ivanhoe*
H *Waverley*
I *The Antiquary*
J *Rob Roy*

3 A Sir Walter Scott
B James Boswell
C William Drummond
D Robert Louis Stevenson
E Robert Burns

4 A James Thomson (1700–48)
B Robert Burns
C James Thomson (1834–82)
D Sir Walter Scott
E James Hogg
F Robert Henryson
G James I, King of Scots
H Thomas Campbell
I Sir David Lyndsay
J John Barbour

Scottish Letters

5   A   *Kidnapped*, by R. L. Stevenson
    B   *The Thirty-Nine Steps*, by John Buchan
    C   *Treasure Island*, by R. L. Stevenson
    D   *The Master of Ballantrae*, by R. L. Stevenson
    E   *Prester John*, by John Buchan

6   A   *Marmion*, by Sir Walter Scott
    B   *From a Railway Carriage*, by R. L. Stevenson
    C   *The Whistle*, by Charles Murray
    D   *Hohenlinden*, by Thomas Campbell
    E   *Sir Patrick Spens*, Anonymous
    F   *Get up and Bar the Door*, Anonymous
    G   *The Battle of Killiecrankie*, by W. E. Aytoun
    H   *Thomas the Rhymer*, Anonymous (sometimes attributed to Scott)
    I   *Tam o' Shanter*, by Robert Burns

7   A   William Wordsworth
    B   Gerard Manley Hopkins
    C   William Collins
    D   John Keats
    E   Thomas Babbington Macaulay (some would count Macaulay a Scot, for, although he was born in England, he came of a Scottish family)
    F   Lord Byron
    G   Wilfrid Wilson Gibson
    H   Robert Southey

[7] I   Sir. F. H. Doyle (If you do not know why this topic is of interest to Scots, see *Scotland in Arms*, question 5)
    J   Charles Wolfe

8   A   James Hogg
    B   Sir Walter Scott (Sheriff of Selkirkshire)
    C   Robert Burns (taken from his own poem)
    D   Sir David Lyndsay (so called in *Marmion*)

9   A   The gay goshawk
    B   Lord Randall's (or Ronald's) mother
    C   One of the Twa Corbies
    D   Lord Marmion
    E   Lord Ronald Macdonald

10   A   Sir James G. Frazer
    B   James Boswell
    C   Adam Smith
    D   Thomas Carlyle
    E   David Hume

11   A   William Sharp
    B   O. H. Mavor
    C   C. M. Grieve
    D   John Wilson
    E   H. H. Munro (born in England of Highland parents)

12   William Miller

13   A   *Lock the Door, Lariston*, by James Hogg
    B   *Requiem*, by R. L. Stevenson
    C   *A Border Burn*, by J. B. Selkirk
    D   *Auld Robin Gray*, by Lady Anne Barnard
    E   *Ae Fond Kiss*, by Robert Burns

Scottish Letters

[13] F *The Land o' the Leal*, by
Lady Carolina Nairne

G *Invocation* or *Summons to Love*, by William Drummond

H *Coronach*, by Sir Walter Scott

I *The Maid of Neidpath*, by Thomas Campbell

14 A James Thomson
B James Bridie
C John Home
D Allan Ramsay
E J. M. Barrie

15 A Sir Henry Lee's greyhound in Scott's *Woodstock*

B The ploughman's collie in Burns' *The Twa Dogs* and Cuthullin's dog in Macpherson's *Ossian*

C Douglas's hound in Scott's *Lady of the Lake*

D Dandy Dinmont's terriers in Scott's *Guy Mannering*

E In John Brown's *Rab and His Friends*

F Scott's favourite hound

16 A Burns
B Scott
C R. L. Stenenson
D Carlyle

17 The Byre Theatre, St. Andrews

18 A work claiming to be translations from an ancient Gaelic poet called Ossian, whose genuineness has been hotly disputed

19 A school of writers who took their subjects from humble Scottish life

20 The Lee Penny

21 A rhymster associated with Dundee and famed for his bad verses

22 Gavin Douglas

23 Jane Welsh Carlyle

24 A *Johnie Faa*
B *Tibbie Fowler*
C *The Water o' Wearie's Well*
D *The Daemon Lover*
E *The Wife of Usher's Well*
F *Earl Mar's Daughter*
G *The Twa Corbies*
H *The Laird o' Logie*

25 Wee wee man

26 Early *nom de plume* of O. H. Mavor (James Bridie)

27 Andrew Lang

Scottish Sport

1 A Paisley
B Perth
C Greenock
D Kirkcaldy
E Edinburgh
F Methil
G Dumfries
H Glasgow

2 A Golf
B Hammer throwing and other heavyweight events
C Association football
D Ice hockey
E Distance running
F Rugby Union football

83

Scottish Sport

[2] G Cricket
  H Billiards and snooker
  I Boxing
  J Swimming
3 A Curling
  B Association football
  C Horse racing
  D Rugby Union
  E Fishing
  F Golf
  G Climbing
  H Cricket
4 A Partick Thistle
  B Clyde
  C Dumbarton
  D Forfar Athletic
  E Queen's Park
  F Third Lanark
  G Dunfermline Athletic
  H Queen of the South
  I Ayr United
  J Aberdeen
  K Motherwell
  L Montrose
  M Falkirk
  N St. Mirren
  O Arbroath
5 Rangers and Celtic
6 1902. It was the collapse of a terracing, 25 killed, 618 injured
7 Kilmarnock plays on Rugby Park
8 Queen's Park
9 36. Arbroath, 36; Bon Accord, 0, in 1885
10 Alan Morton (30)
11 149,547 Hampden Park, Scotland v. England, 1937
12 The old type of gutta-percha golf ball
13 Tom Morris, junior, 1868, aged eighteen

14 A golf course, one of the four in St. Andrews, and also a tournament played on that course
15 Prestwick (1860)
16 The Honourable Company of Edinburgh Golfers (formerly the Gentlemen Golfers) founded in 1744
17 The Royal and Ancient Golf Club, St. Andrews
18 Swimming
19 Golf (Carnoustie)
20 The Ecurie Ecosse
21 1872 (Score 0–0). Queen's Park provided the whole of the Scottish side
22 Curling
23 A sailing regatta
24 The Royal Company of Archers
25 A long trimmed pole, the trunk of a tree, tossed in a traditional highland athletic event
26 Archery
27 Rugby Union Football
28 Dick McTaggart of Dundee Boxing
29 12th August, opening of the grouse shooting season
30 For Rugby Union between Scotland and England
31 Hamilton Racecourse
32 A stag carrying twelve points on its horns
33 Curling
34 Shinty

Music and Dancing

1 Strathspey and reel

2 The classical form of bagpipe music

3 A famous fiddler who composed and collected hundreds of dance tunes

4 A small Celtic harp

5 Two Highland broadswords or a sword and its scabbard crossed. This is the Highland Sword Dance.

6 The mouth music tunes of the Highlands, often used for dancing when no instrumentalist is available

7 Pas de Basque

8 A folk song, so called from its being sung in the bothy (cottage) rather than in the concert hall.

9 Mendelssohn's Third Symphony

10 The melody pipe on which the tune is fingered in playing bagpipes

11 Scottish Gaelic minstrelsy, both musical and literary

12 The Great Highland Bagpipe

13 Collecting Scottish folk songs, especially those of the Hebrides

14 The famous Glasgow choir directed by Sir Hugh Roberton

15 The famous psalm tune most commonly used with Psalm

[15] 23 (metrical version), 'The Lord's my shepherd, I'll not want.'

16 The spirit of a person who died was reputed to travel home beneath the earth.

17 William Douglas of Fingland who married Elizabeth Clerk of Glenboig while Annie, daughter of Sir Robert Laurie of Maxwelton, married Alexander Fergusson of Craigdarroch

18 The Wee Cooper o' Fife

19 A Highland musical gathering at which the participants pass the evening with informal contributions

20 Fair Kirconnel lea

21 A Highland funeral dirge

22 'Scots Wha Hae'

23 In music, a short note on the beat with a long one occupying the rest of the beat; it gives a peculiarly Scottish lilt.

24 'We're no awa' tae bide awa' '

25 A process of fulling (thickening) cloth. Many folk songs were composed to accompany this process

26 Loch Lomond

27 Scottish National Orchestra

28 'Miracle in the Gorbals'

29 Edinburgh concert hall

30 Sir Harry Lauder

Music and Dancing

31
A *Jock o' Hazledean*
B *Annie Laurie*
C *Bonnie Dundee*
D *Auld Lang Syne*
E *There's Nae Luck aboot the Hoose*
F *Lochaber no more*

[31]
G *Blue Bonnets over the Border*
H *The Skye Boat Song*
I *Will Ye No Come Back Again?*
J *Doun the Burn, Davie Lad*
K *The Flowers o' the Forest*
L *The Bonnie Earl o' Moray*
M *Comin' through the Rye*

Famous Scots

1
A The steam engine
B Television
C Radar
D Road-surfacing
E Extraction of paraffin from shale
F Pneumatic tyres
G The telephone
H The threshing machine

2
A Ballet, theatre and film
B Poetry, classical scholarship and Scottish nationalism
C Theatre
D Music
E Politics, national and local
F Literature
G Natural history
H Academic, Principal and Vice-Chancellor of Glasgow University
I Association football
J Industry

3
A Invented logarithms
B Pioneered chloroform
C Discovered penicillin
D Discovered that the mosquito was the carrier of malaria

4
A Blantyre
B Dunfermline

[4]
C Newark, Foulshiels
D Kirriemuir
E Ecclefechan

5
A Painting
B Speed record breaking (of Scottish parentage)
C Missionary work
D Photography
E The Church, leader of those who founded the Free Church of Scotland
F Political economy
G Exploration of Canada
H Army. Commander-in-chief on the western front in 1914–18 war

6 William Thomson, Lord Kelvin

7 John Paul Jones, after whom the dance is named

8 Alexander Selkirk

9 Alexander Cruden

10 Lord Boyd Orr

11 Great Scottish physicians and surgeons of the eighteenth century. William's bequest founded the Hunterian Museum

12 James Clerk Maxwell

Famous Scots

13 John Law

14 Robert the Bruce

15 James Keir Hardie

16 Sir Harry Lauder

17 James Bruce

18 The Boys' Brigade

19 David Livingstone. Zambesi River in Rhodesia

20 Sir Thomas Lipton

21 Three. Balfour, Campbell-Bannerman and Ramsay Macdonald. Bonar Law, a Glasgow merchant, born in New Brunswick, might be claimed as a fourth

22 John Buchan, Lord Tweedsmuir

23 Chief Scout

24 Mungo Park

25 Two paintings by famous nineteenth-century Scottish artists

26 James McGill

27 James Rennie

28 He was an artist

29 John Brown

30 Donald Smith, Lord Strathcona

31 A pioneer modern architect, working principally in Glasgow

32 James Crichton, a remarkable scholar, linguist and all-rounder, who was killed in Italy in 1582 at the age of twenty-one

33 Duns Scotus

34 Governor-General of India

35 John McDowall Stuart

36 A famous Scottish pirate

37 A Sir Walter Scott
   B Robert Burns
   C Colonel James Cameron, killed at Bull Run, 1861
   D John Knox
   E James V

38 A John Knox
   B Claverhouse
   C Bonnie Prince Charlie
   D Mary Queen of Scots

Land of Scotland

1 A Inverness
  B Musselburgh
  C Dumfries
  D Edinburgh
  E Peterhead
  F Kirriemuir
  G Aberdeen
  H Kirkcaldy (sometimes used of Auchterarder)
  I Oban
  J Perth

2 A Glasgow Cathedral
  B St. Giles Cathedral, Edinburgh
  C Orchanton Round Tower
  D Glasgow University

3 A Suilven
  B Schiehallion
  C Cobbler
  D Ben Nevis

Land of Scotland

4
- A Forth
- B Spey
- C Tay
- D South Esk
- E Clyde
- F Tweed
- G Nith
- H Teviot
- I Dee
- J Garry

5
- A Forfar
- B Stonehaven
- C Inveraray
- D Elgin
- E Dingwall
- F Duns
- G Wick
- H Cupar

6
- A Ben Vorlich, 3,092 feet
- B West Lomond, 1,712 feet
- C Ben Lawers, 3,984 feet
- D Ben Nevis, 4,406 feet
- E Broad Law, 2,754 feet
- F Ben Lomond, 3,192 feet

7
- A Kirkwall
- B Portree
- C Stornaway
- D Tobermory
- E Lerwick

8
- A Gorge, near Ullapool, Ross and Cromarty
- B Rocky islet, just outside the Firth of Clyde
- C Waterfalls on the Clyde
- D A hill

9
- A Islay
- B Mull (Tobermory Bay)
- C Iona
- D St. Kilda (Wren)
- E Inchcolm

10
- A Loch Fyne (sea loch)
- B Loch Linnhe (sea loch)
- C Loch Tay
- D Loch Earn
- E Loch Ness

11
- A Cairngorms (Grampians)
- B Arran Mountains
- C Cuillins (Skye)

12
- A Ben Nevis
- B Ben Loyal

13 Moscow is a village in Ayrshire and St. Helena is an island at the head of Luce Bay, Wigtownshire

14 Culbin Sands

15 32

16 Bute, Orkney and Shetland

17 Inverness

18 Clackmannan

19 Lanarkshire

20 Kinross

21 Dunnet Head, Caithness

22 Tay

23 Inchmurrin

24 Ben Nevis (4,406 feet)

25 Loch Morar

26 Loch Lomond

27 St. Kilda (over 1,300 ft)

28 Buchan Ness

29 Harris and Lewis

30 Glasgow

31 The coastal plain on the north bank of the Tay between Perth and Dundee

32 Staffa

Land of Scotland

33 A loch, the Nor' Loch

34 A Midlothian
   B West Lothian
   C East Lothian

36 A A deep hollow among the hills near Moffat, often the hiding-place for stolen cattle
   B A waterfall in Moffat Dale

36 Eigg

37 A Wallace Monument, Stirling
   B Burns Memorial, Ayr
   C Mercat Cross, Culross

38 Muckle Flugga Lighthouse

39 Near Loch Lomond

40 Wanlockhead, Dumfries-shire

41 Twelve are listed in *Munro's Tables*, but three are on

[41] Ben Macdhui, three on Braeriach and two on Cairn Toul. We may therefore reduce the number to seven: Ben Nevis, 4,406 ft; Ben Macdhui, 4,296 ft; Braeriach, 4,248 ft; Cairn Toul, 4,241 ft; Cairngorm, 4,084 ft; Aonach Beag, 4,060 ft; Carn Mor Dearg, 4,012 ft

42 Oban

43 The Cheviots

44 Famous Rapids on the Aberdeenshire Dee, spanned by a bridge, over which runs the main road

45 A Outer Hebrides
   B Orkney
   C Inner Hebrides
   D Shetland

Robert Burns

1 Alloway, Ayrshire

2 25th January, the anniversary of his birth in 1759

3 Excise Officer

4 *The Scots Musical Museum* and Thomson's *Select Scottish Airs*

5 The Kilmarnock Edition

6 *Poems, Chiefly in the Scottish Dialect*

7 A farm near Mauchline which Burns rented with his brother, Gilbert

8 Jean Armour

9 A cottage in Mauchline, scene of *The Jolly Beggars*

10 It is his birthplace in Alloway

11 Some hae meat an' canna eat,
   And some wad eat that want it,
   But we hae meat an' we can eat,
   And sae the Lord be thankit
   Usually attributed to Burns and said at all Burns suppers

Robert Burns

12 A Scots, wha hae wi' Wallace bled, . . .
   B John Anderson my jo, John, . . .
   C Let other poets raise a fracas . . .
   D Ae fond kiss, and then we sever!
   E Is there for honest poverty . . .
   F There was three kings into the east, . . .
   G O, my luve's like a red, red rose, . . .

13 A Green grow the rashes, O;
     Green grow the rashes, O;
     The sweetest hours that e'er I spend,
     Are spent among the lasses, O
   B Ca' the yowes to the knowes,
     Ca' them whare the heather grows,
     Ca' them whare the burnie rowes,
     My bonie dearie!
   C Sae rantingly, sae wantonly,
     Sae dauntingly gaed he,
     He play'd a spring, and danced it round
     Below the gallows-tree
   D And for auld lang syne, my jo,
     For auld lang syne,
     We'll tak a cup o' kindness yet,
     For auld lang syne
   E My heart's in the Highlands, my heart is not here,

[13E] My heart's in the Highlands a-chasing the deer,
     A-chasing the wild deer and following the roe—
     My heart's in the Highlands, wherever I go!
   F O, whistle an' I'll come to ye, my lad!
     O, whistle an' I'll come to ye, my lad!
     Tho' father an' mother an' a' should gae mad,
     O, whistle an' I'll come to ye, my lad!

14 A *Tam o' Shanter*
   B *The Twa Dogs*
   C *The Cotter's Saturday Night*
   D *Man was Made to Mourn*
   E *Highland Mary*
   F *The Holy Fair*
   G *First Epistle to J. Lapraik*
   H *The Banks o' Doon*

15 A A wounded hare
   B Tam o' Shanter
   C The Deil
   D Edinburgh
   E Maggie, an old mare, addressed in the character of 'an auld farmer'
   F A haggis
   G A mouse

16 A *To a Mouse: on turning her up in her nest with the plough, November 1785*
   B *To a Louse: on seeing one on a lady's bonnet at church*

17 Dumfries

Scotland at Work

1. A Jute—Dundee
    B Linoleum—Kirkcaldy
    C Shawls—Paisley
    D Tweed—Harris
    E Knitwear—Hawick
    F Silk—Dunfermline
    G Sugar—Greenock
    H Aluminium—Fort William
    I Glass bottles—Alloa
    J Ships—Clydebank

2. A Green
    B Black
    C Blue
    D Red

3. *Queen Elizabeth*

4. Jute, Calcutta being the chief Indian mart and site of mills

5. A A primitive foot plough still occasionally used in remoter parts
    B Small stacks of hay
    C Platforms of peat and seaweed or manure built up on poor soil shallow ploughed: generally used to grow potatoes

6. Robert Owen's model mills and industrial community

7. The adjacent Carse of Gowrie is a soft-fruit growing area

8. Farm buildings

9. Thread-making and distilling respectively

10. Fair Isle

11. A *Cutty Sark*
    B *The Comet*
    C H.M.S. *Vanguard*
    D R.M.S. *Queen Mary*

12. A sheep. These hills are famous for sheep-farming

13. To build in granite from the great Rubislaw quarry, Aberdeen

14. A long-handled hammer for breaking stones

15. Extraction of salt from sea water in salt pans

16. An old type of naval gun, made at Carron ironworks, Stirlingshire

17. Land where the alternate ridges or strips of a field belonged to different owners

18. The Bank of Scotland, the Royal Bank of Scotland, the National Bank of Scotland, the Commercial Bank of Scotland, the British Linen Bank, the Clydesdale and North of Scotland Bank

19. It is conveniently situated for the Baltic pulp trade

20. An atomic power station

21. Hydro-electric schemes

22. Lace

23. Golf-club making. They are both golfing centres

24. Whaling

Scotland at Work

25 A Ayrshire
    B Highland
    C Belted Galloway
    D Aberdeen Angus

26 They are all potatoes, for which Scotland is famous

27 Dundee, where D. C. Thomson print a large number of widely circulating periodicals of these classes

28 Glasgow early traded with the West Indies

29 Aberdeen

30 Famous printers in Glasgow in eighteenth century. Scotland is famous for her printers

31 It was Scotland's great west coast port of trade with America

Traditions of the Highlands and Islands

1 The Drinking Horn of a famous Dunvegan chief of the MacLeods, to be drained at a draught by each heir on succeeding to the chieftainship

2 The Churchyard, Balquhidder

3 Piping. They were the hereditary pipers to the McLeods of Dunvegan

4 A wooden cross, the extremities seared in fire, dipped in the blood of a goat slain by a chief and carried round the country-side to summon his clan in arms

5 The Clan Gregor or MacGregor whose name was suppressed by Act of Parliament in the eighteenth century

6 A river spirit, often seen as a water horse

7 Shetland. It marks the end of Yuletide

8 Norse, *Trolls*. Fairy folk of Orkney and Shetland, who love music and dancing and can interfere in the affairs of men

9 Sir Robert Stout

10 Famous brooch of Robert the Bruce, used for fastening his plaid and lost to John, Lord of Lorne, at the Battle of Dalrigh. Now in the possession of MacDougall of MacDougall

11 Lismore. St. Columba and St. Moluag. St. Moluag cut off the little finger of his left hand and threw it ashore, thus claiming to have landed first

12 Tiree

13 Muck (Gaelic *muc*—pig)

14 Canna. Iron deposits in its rocks deflect the compass point

15 St. Francis's Cave, also known as MacDonald or

Traditions of the Highlands and Islands

[15] Clan Ranald Cave. The MacDonalds of Eigg were suffocated by a fire lit at its entrance by the raiding McLeods of Skye

16 A flag of disputed origin kept by the McLeods of Dunvegan and having the power to avert disaster to the clan when it is waved

17 A cascade in a stream adjacent to Dunvegan Castle

18 The Lord of the Isles who in 1346 reduced the Hebrides under his sway

19 A wailing spirit foretelling death

20 Jan Teit

21 The King of Norway formerly ruled over Orkney and Shetland

22 To prevent its being stolen by the Little Folk

23 National Museum of Antiquities, Edinburgh. It was supposed to have contained the mortal remains of St. Columba

24 The Inverewe Gardens planted by Henry Osgood MacKenzie

25 John MacPherson of Glendale, Skye, who incited the people of his district against the landlords, and was imprisoned

26 A war galley of the type formerly used in the Western Isles

27 A thicket of hollies high on the slopes of Ben Alder in which Charles Edward Stewart was in hiding for a time

28 Pass of Killiecrankie

29 Each new bishop of Orkney drank from it and his manner of doing so was construed as an augury for his period of office

30 A famous Gaelic poet revered among Gaelic speakers as Burns is in the Lowlands

31 The aurora borealis

32 At the northern entrance to Bergen harbour, Norway

33 Kirkwall

34 A large community of clans embracing Macphersons, MacGillivrays, Farquharsons, McQuins, McPhails, MacBains and others

35 The equivalent of a Parliament

36 The Marquis of Zetland

37 Orcadians

38 Sigurd, carrying the head of his enemy, Maelbrigte, at his saddle bow, punctured his leg on a projecting tooth and died of the ensuing bloodpoisoning

39 A pillar of detached cliff 450 feet high, Island of Hoy

Traditions of the Highlands and islands

40 When such a price was set on the head of Prince Charles Edward Stewart none betrayed him

41 The Clan Cameron

42 The Macdonalds of Glencoe

43 Flora Macdonald

Speirin' Loons

1 Asking questions

2 Fort William and Inverness

3 Loch Faskally

4 Glen Lyon

5 Glasgow

6 Dunfermline

7 Princess Royal Park

8 The Orkney Islands, near Cava

9 A gad-fly

10 Neil M. Gunn

11 Poetry

12 *Hatter's Castle*

13 30,405 square miles

14 5,098,969 (1951)

15 71

16 1817

17 From the dark tartan of its kilt

18 Kilpatrick

19 Parts of the old walls of Edinburgh

20 *The Well at the World's End* and *The Drinking Well*

21 A Ptarmigan
   B Golden Eagle
   C Black Grouse
   D Hooded Crow

22 A Curling Stone
   B Sporran
   C Claymore
   D Coracle
   E Quaich

23 A hospitable and hearty draught of liquor

24 1893: W. Auchterlonie

25 6. Edinburgh, Glasgow, Aberdeen, Dundee, Perth and Elgin

26 The Plateau of Braeriach

27 Loch Rannoch

28 Dumbarton (1890–91)

29 Loch Leven (Fife)

30 The Royal Company of Archers

31 Iona

32 The Firth of Clyde, The Firth of Lorne, The Pentland Firth, The Dornoch Firth, The Cromarty Firth, The Firth, The Beauly Firth, The Firth of Tay, The Firth of Forth

33 Scottish Youth Hostels Association

34 The Scottish Mountaineering Club

35 A mixture of whisky, honey and oatmeal

Speirin' Loons

36 The Clan Campbell

37 Periods when Scotland on
average has a compara-
tively cold spell of weather
for the time of year.
They were first plotted
by Alexander Buchan, a
former secretary of the
Scottish Meteorological
Society

38 Two. That of Kirkcud-
bright and that of
Orkney and Shetland

39 James V

40 Whisky

41 John Gibson Lockhart

42 The double peninsula on
which stands Stranraer

43 Glencoe

44 6th December, 1745, the
day on which news

[44] reached London that
Prince Charles Edward
had reached Derby

45 We mean that it turns in a
contrary direction to the
movement of the sun and
it is held to imply that
the most evil luck is
about to befall the rider

46 A circular hollow in a
mountainside (compare
Welsh *cwm*)

47 John Arbuthnot

48 High Street, Edinburgh

49 21st June

50 Orkney, on the way to
Scotland's throne, 1293

51 Dunstaffnage Castle

52 Do not vex (or inconveni-
ence) yourself

Finding Things out in Scotland

1 The National Portrait
Gallery of Scotland in
Edinburgh

2 *The Scottish National
Dictionary* is in the
process of publication and
so far three volumes are
available. Another large
dictionary is Jamieson's
*Dictionary of the Scottish
Language,* while
*Chambers's Scots Dialect
Dictionary* is a handy
single volume

3 The Scottish Central
Library, a Carnegie
foundation. Such a
library is very necessary
in a country with many
thinly populated areas

4 *Chambers's Twentieth
Century Dictionary*

5 Sir James Murray. *The
Oxford English Dictionary*
(O.E.D.), often called
'Murray's Dictionary'

Finding things out in Scotland

Printed in Great Britain by
Jarrold and Sons Limited · Norwich